LUSH LIFE

Lush Life

A Collection of Short Stories by

TINKA HARVARD

Adelaide Books
New York / Lisbon
2018

LUSH LIFE
a collection of short stories by
Tinka Harvard

Published by Adelaide Books, New York / Lisbon
adelaidebooks.org

Editor-in-Chief
Stevan V. Nikolic

For any information, please address Adelaide Books
at info@adelaidebooks.org
or write to:
Adelaide Books
244 Fifth Ave. Suite D27
New York, NY, 10001

ISBN13: 978-1-949180-11-4
ISBN10: 1-949180-11-5

Printed in the United States of America

For Mom and for Auntie

Contents

Lullaby
Same Story, Two Perspectives

Momma

I never talked about him to my children except when I would tell them about the night we all left him. We snuck out of town in the middle of the night while he was in the hospital.

No one thought he would live. None of the doctors thought he would survive.

He came home one night drunk and started beating on me again. I was sitting by the window in the kitchen nursing my baby girl. He knocked her out of my arms and continued punching on me. He used to beat my ass for breakfast, lunch, and dinner. Something came over me this time. I grabbed a knife and stabbed him. I grabbed my babies, all three of them, and ran out of the house and down the road to my mother's house.

When my mother got to the hospital to see about him, they told her they didn't think he would make it. Turns out I had stabbed him half an inch from his heart. I just missed it.

My mother put me and my children on a bus in the middle of the night to get us out of town. We rode all night, riding to my daddy's house up north. My children slept through the night and woke up with the sun shining in their faces through the bus window.

So our lives went in separate ways. When we got on up north, we were alright in New York City. I felt free. Free from the conflicts of my marriage with him, and even free from the controlling ways of my mother.

My children are good people. I tried to raise them right. I fed them well. I cooked everything myself from scratch. Made sure they got their education. I taught them to be independent. To wait before beginning a family. To live their life, because once the babies come, you will have to sit at home and rock 'em.

My children never showed any interest in meeting their father. I never bad-mouthed him, I simply told them what happened. What happened in the marriage was a lifetime ago. I told them they should meet their father, give him a chance.

Daddy

I was in the hospital fighting for my life. On the way to the hospital, in the ambulance I was thinking there's no way I'm going to survive this.

I was lying there in the hospital thinking I'm not going to make it through. The doctor, he was from Germany. I can still see his face in my mind. He put a tube in my back and drained the blood. That's all I remember before I passed out.

I made it. The day that I got out of the hospital I went home and my family was gone. No one would tell me where they were. It took me years to find out where they had gone. I was heartbroken. I've got a scar, right here, next to my heart.

We were so young. Eighteen when the first baby came. And then two more were born, one right after the other. All of them a year apart. I'd come in from work and get so angry, fed up with her always wanting to go out with her friends. We had babies to take care of. I wish we could do it all over again. I'd do better.

I never thought about pressing charges. I loved her. And more importantly, I didn't want the mother of my children to be taken away. I wanted my children to have their mother. I'm a little nervous, but I'm ready. I'm really excited to meet them. It's been thirty years since I've seen my children.

Lush Life

As a girl, and still, my younger sister was incredibly out-going, courageous and confident, while I was the shy one, and a bit of a loner. Our interests differed. My sister was most often outdoors playing with her friends; running and jumping, navigating the squares of Hopscotch and rhythmically keeping time to the twirling ropes of double Dutch. I was the more timid and quiet one. I spent a lot of time indoors, dreamily pouring over teen magazines, poetry and novels, lost in lyrical tunes and teenage angst.

Outside of our home my sister and I didn't spend much time together, our interests never coincided and this separation seemed to spill over into our adult lives. In connection, while growing up we didn't even fight, there wasn't anything to fight about. In general, we all tend to fight over things we love and want. My sister and I wanted different things, loved different things. The love we have in common is a love for one another.

I remember during an afternoon at a friend's wedding, my sister and I managed to steal some time to ourselves, sneaking away to a corner during cocktail hour, away from the crowd. We had not seen one another for ages, and now was our time to selfishly indulge in the company of one another once again.

Sweet reunions are like this, like in the days just after the violent winds and rains of the now infamous Hurricane Sandy. I called my sister to see how she was coping with the storm. We began to connect all over again, conversing of power outages, causing the light, heat, and hot water to be turned off. Surprisingly, we found ourselves reminiscing about the good ol' days. As the mind can be kind, and quite possibly our memories have been air brushed, where a seemingly impoverished daily existence has become tinged with a touch of a patina of days long gone. We giggled and laughed, remembering our magical endurance of a past life, which on the surface would appear less than glamorous. We marveled at our feats to get warm.

It was not unusual on our way home from school, as we would get closer to our apartment building, to see neighbors communing outside, in the front courtyard of our building. They would inform all concerned that there was no heat or hot water, and no electricity either, throughout the building—the CNN of the neighborhood.

My sister and I each had a key that unlocked the door to our home on a string around our neck. We would let ourselves in to a cold and empty apartment. Stepping into the darkening apartment, the warm glow of the setting sun provided a fleeting light. Over in the cupboard was where we kept candles and matches. We would quickly begin lighting candles, filling our home with a dim light.

In the glow of soft lighting, we would get out of our school uniforms, and wrap ourselves in bathrobes, and begin to prepare our baths. Mom said we had to be bathed and finished with our homework before she came in from work.

For hot water we would heat water on the kitchen stove and transport the warmed water to the bathtub; a claw foot deep bathtub—a deep claw-foot tub, the kind common in prewar buildings in Brooklyn that   also had nine foot ceilings and beautiful parquet floors. Where we lived was a former Jewish neighborhood. The Jewish population had left long ago, either moving closer to Manhattan or on the other side of the Brooklyn Bridge.

In a bit of bird's bath, by the light of soft flickering candles my sister and I bathed while we giggled and talked about what happened at school; who liked who, and who was now dating, and what happened on our math or English quizzes. Once done playing in the shallow bath, we'd step out, our narrow bodies shivering and slick and soapy. We'd quickly wrap themselves in soft cotton towels of our favorite colors. After drying ourselves, we'd put on layers of clothing; cotton knit undergarments and cotton bottoms, and plush sweaters and woolen socks to cushion and warm our feet. We didn't have much, but of the few things we had, our mom tried to buy quality materials. Funnily, in this art of keeping warm, unconsciously and organically we created a kind of fashion or style, a Brooklyn bohemian aesthetic.

We talked of an earlier time, when we were much younger and warm and comfy inside. Saturday nights we participated in a kind of ritual, as it was a weekly occasion when mom spent time dressing to go out on Saturday night. Our home was filled with the scent of pretty perfume and the music of Aretha Franklin and Marvin Gaye, songs like "I Say a Little Prayer" and "How Sweet It Is (To Be Loved by You)." Mom walked around in her slip and pantyhose. This was a time when women wore silk lace slips beneath their dresses. It was an occasion. We were given little chocolates and got to follow mom around the house while she chose what to wear for the evening, put on her makeup and perfume, and styled her hair. We were excited with the goings on. I remember that my sister and I would climb up on the closed toilet seat in our bathroom and have fun trying to keep our balance, teetering on the small space, while watching mom prettying herself up in the bathroom mirror. She applied her lipstick last. It was such a girlish ambiance. Mom would put a little red lipstick on our lips. My sister and I waited for this all day. We would stand there on top of the toilet seat, near to the bathroom mirror, with our lips poking out and our eyes closed as mom rubied our lips. We would stay this way for the rest of the night, walking around barefoot in our panties and T-shirt with ruby red lips until we had to go to bed, which was not very long really, as the babysitter had to have us in bed shortly after our mother left.

My sister and I reminisced about the music playing, our home warm and scented deliciously as our mom slipped into her cocktail dress and high heels for the evening. Her silken pantyhose with a threaded seam down the back of her stockings were the coolest and loveliest things. We would help to get the seam in a straight line. It was a long black line that disappeared down mom's long legs into the back of her high heels. We'd get sweet kisses, filling our cheeks and lips with lipstick as she disappeared out the door seemingly in a gentle cloud of the most delicate and deliciously scented perfume.

I've had a long fascination with the luxurious and visions of beauty, and how they touch our everyday. It is the dreaminess, and an embrace of the lush that attracts me as I remember a particular aesthetic, and attraction to the beautiful in my impoverished environment while growing up.

The Little Shabby Brooklyn Kitchen-
and How to Make Mud Pies

If you were to climb over the short fence into the abandoned lot just off the corner of Livonia Avenue and Sackman Street in Brooklyn, where there once stood an old dilapidated apartment building that had been torn down, there you could find just about all the things you would need to make mud pies, circa 1970, and so much more. Silver spoons, chipped porcelain tea cups, empty soup tins, aluminum pie pans, and dented stainless steel pots—even a floral-print armchair and old tattered white lace curtains—almost everything needed to create a cozy space to enjoy pie and tea on a warm summer day in Brooklyn was right there.

So many shabby treasures existed in the abandoned lots in the neighborhood that you could furnish a home if you needed to. My friends and I made our little Brooklyn kitchen beside this particular abandoned lot. We wanted to stay near it because it served as a kind of supply store for us. Whatever we needed, we could just climb back over the fence and get it. The only thing the lot was lacking was running water.

We got some grownups to bring a castoff armchair over the fence one time, and we left it there beside the lot and tied the corners of lace curtains through the links of the fence adding a nice touch to our dining space.

Good Dirt Mud Pie

This recipe is for making *fine* mud pies, which will require *good dirt*. Good dirt is a soft, clean dirt made from hard, impure earth from the abandoned lot.

First, climb the fence into the abandoned lot and gather all the tools you will need to make mud pies. Then with your four-year-old fingers, sort through the bricks, rocks, broken bits of glass, and metal to get to the earth beneath. Use a spoon or anything else that you can find to dig up the dirt and put it into a tin can or bowl or bucket or pot.

Once you have found all the essential stuff and dug up some dirt, you and your friends can climb back over the fence. The last person can toss the treasures over the fence to the other side before climbing over. You might lose some of the dirt that you've gathered, but that's okay. That's how it goes sometimes. We can lose a few things when trying to do something beautiful.

The freshly dug up dirt will contain rocks, glass, and all sorts of trash, but no worries, you can easily work them out. Find an old discarded window screen—there is bound to be one in the lot. Use it to make good dirt by sifting the impure dirt through the screen. Pass the dirt through the wire mesh a couple times until all the debris is separated from the dirt. The result will be a soft dirt free from other impurities. That's good dirt.

Now find water. If it is a hot summer day, you can get water at an open Johnny pump. If a sprinkler is on the fire hydrant, it can be a bit tricky to get the water into a bucket, but it can be even more fun.

If the hydrants are closed, then trek a few flights upstairs to mom's kitchen or to a friend's apartment on the block to get water. Carefully carry the bucket (or pot or tin can) filled with water back downstairs. It is always good to know the various sources of water—the shortest trip may be to a friend's house—because you will have to haul the water downstairs in the wintertime when the Johnny pumps are closed. But in the wintertime, you can put snow on top of the mud pies, which makes a nice "cream" topping.

Add the water to the good dirt slowly, a little bit at a time. Patiently mix the combination into a fine, smooth mud. It should be the consistency of creamy, warm grits.

Pour the mud into old aluminum pie pans and drag them from the middle of the sidewalk with great care to avoid spilling out the mud. Place them along the apartment building wall out of the way of people walking by.

Sit with your best friends and wait for the pies to bake in the sun. To pass the time, draw hopscotch courts and flowers with pretty chalk colors of pinks and baby blues and tender yellows. Or you can do whatever pleases you or comes to mind while you wait. It may take a while, but it is never too long to wait for something good.

SERVES 4 BEST FRIENDS
Depending on who can come out to play

PREP & BAKING TIME
35 minutes

INGREDIENTS
2 tin cans dirt
2 ½ tin cans water (or more if necessary)
Snow for topping (optional, and only in winter)

Makes one pie

Three Little Birds

The Top-10 Playlist of Lily Eva,
as Heard on the Podcast **Loser's Delight**

The *Loser's Delight* podcast is a series of talks where we ask the unsuccessful and uncelebrated to share the stories that tell of their failings or losing in life. In connection, we ask them to talk about the songs they would choose in making a playlist to reflect those experiences.

Ironically, we are learning that this project inspires and comforts people from all walks of life. Surprisingly, we have received correspondences from A-list celebrities as well. They, too, are fans of our work. It seems they crave the anonymity of being nobody and the luxury and freedom from the pressure of not always getting it right . . . we're all the same.

So, *Listeners,* I know you can imagine our surprise when we got a call from the famously reclusive romantic novelist Lily Eva asking us if she could participate in our podcast. Lily was incredibly generous, sharing and divulging some of her experiences of the times in her life when things did not quite go as she would have liked or dreamed.

We were delighted to learn that she, too, is a fan of *Loser's Delight.* She tunes in to our podcast regularly. She says she finds the personal stories of our guests—the ne'er-do-wells, drifters, and bums doing nothing and going nowhere—liberating because they show that failing is not the end of the world. You know our motto: at rock bottom, things can only improve.

During our talk, we asked Lily how is it that someone like her, an obsessively private, reclusive introvert, feels comfortable sharing such intimate details of her past. She said that she is trying to let go of her past failures and shortcomings. "Your fear will not keep you safe," she quoted the poet and writer Audre Lorde. Lily continued, "And who knows, maybe some young person, some lost soul, will someday stumble upon this talk and find it helpful, or a comfort."

In this podcast, you will hear, in Lily Eva's own words, about her biggest losing moments in this experiment called life. And check out her playlist, "Three Little Birds," to see if one of your favorite songs made the cut.

1. I got lost in Brooklyn, walking in the rain, one Saturday morning on my way to take the SAT exam my senior year of high school. I stopped to ask directions, and the guy I asked happened to be going to take the same exam. He let me walk with him under his umbrella. After the exam he asked if he could see me again. We ended up dating for a couple of years.

Two years into our relationship, while I was living on campus at Columbia, he visited me in my dorm room. That weekend it rained something awful just like the day when we met. He asked me to come home for the weekend so that he could spend time with me, away from my grouchy roommate I guessed. I didn't want to do that. I wanted to stay with my friends and hang around school. He got angry and slapped me hard across my face. It was the first time he had hit me. I was stunned. My mom left an abusive marriage when I was a kid, so I know what leaving a violent relationship looks like. It was just us two alone in my dorm room. I couldn't believe he had hit me.

I told him what he wanted to hear. That is, I said I would come home. I asked him to go on ahead and let me finish up a few things I needed to do for school, and I would meet him later. I did go home to my mom's house that evening, and I invited him over. I wanted to be in a safe space when I told him it was over. Anyone who has met my mother knows not to get on her bad side. Sitting there in my momma's kitchen he apologized for hitting me. He knew from the look on my face that I meant what I said. It was over. So he got up and walked out the door. That was the first and last time I was ever hit. I try to stay away from stuff like that.

The first song on my playlist is "Luka" by Suzanne Vega. A lot of people don't know that this song is about abuse. Abuse is not okay. Everyone deserves respect. The music and lyrics of "Luka" are deceptively melodic and serene. Spooky once one learns what the song is about.

2. I enjoyed living on campus during college and being away from home. I remember during freshman orientation one of the orientation leaders told us to look around the room. He said many of the freshman would not make it to graduation. I remember the sadness and shock that ran through me when he said that. I loved school and the possibilities an education can bring in life. How sad that, for all the many reasons, not everyone would get the privilege of an education. I made a pact with myself that it would not be me, that I would not be one of the ones not to make it through. I had a couple close calls when I didn't have the money for tuition fees. I ended up working three part-time jobs during college, and I made it through.

I loved dancing on Saturday nights at campus parties. Michael Jackson's "Smooth Criminal" was my favorite during this time. That's number two on my playlist.

3. I was an English major, and one of my part-time jobs was an internship at a major publishing company. I remember hearing Steve Winwood's "Higher Love" for the first time on a little portable radio that my boss kept on her office desk. I liked that song immediately when I heard it. I liked it a lot. It may sound a bit strange, but during those college years, I was just learning about pop music. We always listened to soul music and jazz in our home. I grew up on the tunes of Aretha Franklin and John Coltrane, beautiful songs like "I Say a Little Prayer" and albums like *A Love Supreme.* Away from home, I was beginning to expand my musical experience. "Higher Love" is my number three pick.

4. One of my best friends was studying law at Harvard. I used to visit her often in Cambridge. What a pretty place. Surprisingly, it's an incredibly difficult environment. The competition of the students in law school was brutal, so we would go on long car rides to relax. I loved waking up early on a Sunday morning and going for a ride while the sun was rising. On the radio in her car we listened to Depeche Mode, The Pet Shop Boys, Duran Duran, The Cure. Good stuff!

I haven't been to Cambridge since my friend graduated, but I will always treasure the memory of those sunrise rides on Sunday mornings and the good music we listened to. Number four in honor of this experience is Depeche Mode's "Enjoy the Silence."

5. After college, I worked for the same publishing company where I had interned during college. I met Gisele one day while reading on the subway on my way to work. We had a lovely conversation, kept in touch, and later became friends. Gisele was from Florence. She was a pianist. I enjoyed going with her to the ballet and classical music performances at Lincoln Center. It was because of her that I learned of Chopin's "Nocturnes" performed by Arthur Rubinstein. It is fifth on my playlist. We used to lay on the parquet floors of my Brooklyn apartment and simply listen to the gentle and tranquil nocturnes. I once said to Gisele that I felt a bit silly since I am not educated in classical music. She said something that serves me well to this day: "But you know what you like. That's all that matters."

6. I left publishing to work in a bookstore while I tried to figure out what I wanted to be when I grew up. (It turns out that I wanted to write books myself.) People think that working in a bookstore is sweet with all the romantic notions that come with thoughts of the literary world. Their thoughts of books are connected to the stories within them—fantasy and fairy tales, people falling in love, action and adventure—but working in a bookstore is deceptively hard work. Think about it. Think about how heavy boxes of books are. Truckloads of books were delivered every day to the stockroom. The guys in the stockroom would unpack them and enter them into the computer for inventory purposes. Their job was the hardest. Still, there was always a good vibe back in the stockroom. The guys had their music going on the radio while they unpacked the boxes, and they were super friendly and kind.

We, the booksellers, would then haul the books out onto the floor of the bookstore. Those books were heavy. Even if we used carts to transport them, they were still heavy. And being on your feet all day was difficult too. Sorting and shelving books coupled with being on your feet all day makes for a long and physical day. But I loved being around books, and we had a good atmosphere in the store. True story: I was in the store one night when one of the most famous people in the world came in with his entourage. This was a posh store on the upper east side of Manhattan. I was working the closing shift. When the store closed at ten, a couple of us had to hang around to straighten things up and make the store presentable for the early morning opening. That night while we were putting books back in place, our manager said that someone would be coming in while we were tidying up the store and we were not to bother him. It was ten at night, and we were exhausted. We had no interest in interacting with the lucky person who would have the run of the store to shop after-hours. That sentiment changed once we saw that it was Michael Jackson. We didn't bother him though. He browsed the shelves while we straightened them up. He bought about $700 worth of books, mostly self-help and philosophy stuff. A couple of people asked for his autograph. He was sweet, really.

It was while working in the bookstore that I stumbled across the writings of Thomas Merton. While reading his books I realized that I wanted to write like Thomas Merton. I applied to and began studying at a seminary. I learned quickly that there is only one Thomas Merton. Still I try to write in a way that I hope inspires and informs in a meaningful way.

It was at seminary that I started listening to Enya. She's a singer that lives a reclusive life in a castle somewhere in the mountains of Ireland. Sounds like heaven to me because I enjoy solitude immensely. Enya is good for the heart. Her music is ridiculously beautiful and soothing. There's something satisfying about a woman creating and sharing beauty in this world, and at the same time staying away from the stresses of society. She inspires me with her songs. "Only Time," in particular, is most gorgeous and a perfect addition, number six, for my playlist.

7. I also stumbled upon James Michener's book *Iberia,* when I was in seminary. It wasn't assigned reading. I was reading it for pleasure. Michener wrote in this book that every writer should go to Spain. This statement got to me. So I went.

There I listened to Bebe. Her music will surprise you. It's fast and quirky and smart. Her song "Malo" fits this time in my life well. It captures the Spanish idea of *duende,* the quality of passion and inspiration. The tune, ironically, is upbeat and fun to listen to, but the lyrics are heartbreaking, capturing the spirit of the difficulty of finding our way in the world in the midst of fear and violence. Spain is like that. It captures the heaviness that life can sometimes be, the longing for something better, and the promise of something good.

8. I taught English while I was in Madrid. I wasn't any good at it, but native English speakers willing to work for ten euro an hour could easily find clients. Luckily, my students liked me because I really didn't know how to teach English. My students were engineers who had spent nearly a lifetime repeatedly studying English grammar, but we didn't have much of that in class simply because I wasn't equipped to teach it. Many of us know what it's like to study a foreign language for years and still feel like we can't speak it. Unlike all their previous English classes, my class was more philosophical. We read, among other things, classic American literature like *Catcher in the Rye*, and I would have them write about their reflections on the reading assignments. And we would have discussions on various topics from pop culture to the meaning of life. They liked the different and quirky nature of my class, which better enabled them to practice and improve their language skills. So we enjoyed wonderful discussions in class, and they grew in courage and fluency.

I thought I should grow up and stop living this bohemian life as an expat abroad. I thought I should come home and get a real job. When I returned home, I couldn't find work and fell into a depression. While I was in Spain, Corinne Baily Rae's song "Put Your Records On" was everywhere. It's the cutest song about the idea of listening to music when we are sad and depressed, and in time, things will work out. When I listen to this song, which I am adding to my playlist to represent this life experience, I'm reminded of Bob Marley's "Three Little Birds," from which Rae took inspiration for her song, where he sings "don't worry 'bout a thing."

9. In "All That You Have Is Your Soul," Tracy Chapman's sings about how we need to honor ourselves and that we need to learn in life not to give the essence of who we are away. Simply put, we need to take care of ourselves. Inspirational writer Julia Cameron shares the idea of an artist's date. We can take ourselves out and allow this time on our own to inspire and teach us the things that will serve us well in life. I transformed this idea to suit my situation at the time. I went out on my own. I walked in Central Park, visited the Guggenheim and the Museum of Modern Art. I took in my share of Broadway theater and passed time on the Highline. Ironically, that's when I began to write earnestly. I simply put my bottom in the chair, and I wrote. "All That You Have Is Your Soul," number nine on my playlist, is a heartfelt lesson and reminder to not always give away all that we are and to honor our deepest selves.

10. In time, you get to know that you are enough. You learn in life, as Veronica Shoffstall says in her poem "After a While," to "plant your own garden and decorate your own soul." After all this time, I am learning to not look to others to fill me up. There is the idea to "be still and know." In stillness and quiet, sitting in meditation, I get to know the rhythms of my heart. I'm not sure where I will go from here in life, but maybe being a little older and a little wiser will help me to be good to myself.

I'm choosing "Green & Gold" by Lianne La Havas as my tenth and final song on this playlist. She's a singer that I've recently been listening to. I love her youth and vitality and message of embracing and celebrating who you are.

Thank you, listeners, for allowing me to contribute. If you tell me your story, I will tell you mine.

The Guardian of the Seraglio
(The Moorish Chief)

I began walking some years ago to walk off my angst during a difficult time. Turns out a certain kind of sadness can only be assuaged by the acts of the body in motion. The movements as well as the sights going by helped to ease what hurt.

It hurt too much to keep still. I began to walk as a kind of ritual, a meditation, which began to take on its own special meaning and intentions. I was walking to work things out. Wholly lost in my thoughts, I walked quietly, slowly, without speaking to anyone; a silent unconscious agreement between my heart and whoever else might be interested. Perhaps until something welled up inside and needed to have its say.

I'd wake up each morning and cry. Is this it? I'd ask myself. My plans for a career in finance seemed foolish now. I was young and idealistic. Now I felt broken. I could barely sleep. Seven years after university, seven years of getting up every day and my mission in life was to help other people to figure out how to take care of their money. Only I had not anticipated the greed and aggression that lives in the money world. Naïveté and youth are sisters. I found myself heartbroken and disillusioned. I think I even cried for that which I was still unconscious of.

I tried to talk to the people I love about needing to quit my job, resign was far too delicate a word, I needed to quit. I needed to do something sure and determined, to end it.

I would get talked out of it, as it was said I was being irresponsible. I would ruin my career was the consensus.

These were the reasons people who loved me gave as to why I should not walk away from work that felt like it was draining the life out of me. I felt trapped and confused. So I walked as a prescription for what ailed me.

It was a thing that came as a surprise that saved me. While walking I happened upon a gallery in New York. Suddenly I came out of my thoughts to notice an image in a gallery window. How curious this thing was.

I stepped inside and asked the gallery attendant. "Please sir, could you tell me about this image?"

"*The Moorish Chief,*" he shares as if he knows a secret he's eager to reveal. That he's only been waiting for one who would ask for entry into sacred space, open to anyone who should delight in entering. I had never heard of the word Moor. This one who stands in front, who is he? I marveled.

The curator went on to explain that the Moors, Muslims, were from north western Africa and were in Spain around seven to eight hundred years after the birth of Christ, and this image was a copy of the original which resides in The Philadelphia Museum of Art.

Really? I think. *Sure?* Is my second thought. "Africans in Spain?"

"Yup," he says.

I later learn more. The painting, also known as *The Guardian of the Seraglio;* the guardian, in white flowing robes, with a kind of hooded cloak, stands in front of the Seraglio, the name for the special quarters in a Muslim residence where the women of the household were sheltered from strangers. The guardian; is a protector of women in the palace.

In the background of the painting, he is standing in front of a Moorish palace which would have been created late in Spain's Islamic era, based on the Alhambra, a famous fortress overlooking the city of Granada, Spain.

The impression the painting left on me was of a palace in the background with a harmonious synthesis of space and light, high tiled walls and soft, lush, flowing water that sought to conjure the gardens of paradise. There were expanses of tile, muqarnas, mesmerizing as the intricate stucco work adorned the walls with Arabic inscriptions, covering nearly every surface in calligraphy, transforming the words from ritual praise into geometric pattern.

The symmetrical doorways were also framed with glazed tiles and stucco, a continuing lace like detail, and another assembly of calligraphy. Panels of colored glass set in the ceiling cast a warm glow throughout the quarters, making up one of the finest Islamic structures in Europe.

I was drawn there, still, in the presence of the painting. I stood there and just watched for some time. Reluctantly, yet grateful, I left the gallery.

At work, on the subway, on my way home, in the shower, while reading, during everyday doings, I found that, I could not get that image out of my mind. It was a needed comfort and relief.

This Spain, what's it all about? I wondered. In a bookstore I reached for a few guide books of Spain. I choose ones with more words than pictures, some with far more pictures than words. Sitting down in the bookstore café, steaming cup of tea nearby, I begin to turn the pages. I honed in closer, studying every word, every picture carefully, as if I were a scientist peering at a specimen through a microscope.

The colors of the houses with red roof tops, the architecture, the people and cafés, descriptions of the Spanish culture, I found it all so intriguing. I read about the customs that were difficult for me to wrap my mind around; dinner at ten, but before that, for the most part, forget about it. Can't be, I think. The love and true value of relationships, as family and friendships are adored. I've heard of this in general, but it's not my reality. I live in a city where tenderness and care are wanting, and where time is money and money is time. Where passing long hours in the company of friends is often deemed irrelevant and unproductive.

But in Spain there is delicious food (the water of Valencia makes the most perfect Paella in all of Spain), the architecture of Gaudi, the art of Dali, the thoughtful mind benders of Picasso, or the disturbing images of Goya. Wine vineyards produce wine that rivals Italy and France. Olive tree fields producing, some say, the best olive oil in Europe. People work to live as opposed to live to work, I read on . . . Oh, and a little something about the Mediterranean Sea was mentioned.

These ideas touched me in a way that was almost a tickling, as if by an angel; her leaning over my heart and pursing her lips, blowing on my wounds. Do you know that feeling, when you're bruised and someone who loves you leans in really close and blows gentle breaths right where it hurts and you are soothed . . . comforted?

Ridiculous! Don't be a fool! I say to myself. There's no way a place I know nothing of can possibly touch me where it seems I most need it. But then again, if they've got beautiful architecture like the travel guidebook describes, and Cathedrals decorated outrageously in gold to get God's attention, that even God would say, "Come on!" As it seems that is the legend for one community who would place so much time and attention on beauty. I want to see it too. I want to say "Oh, come on!" in a kind of disbelief at such lavish adornment. I need it as I've been waking up each morning and literally crying while preparing my morning tea and choosing which dress to wear before going to the office. I need to go and see with my own eyes if what they say is true. And to see if the Mediterranean is as blue and as beautiful as they say it is.

Le sentier d'un flâneur
(The Path of the Wanderer)

Initially, I was quite bored of it all until *Casablanca*. My aunt asked me to sit with her and keep her company while she watched her beloved black-and-white movies. The mood and suspense of *Casablanca* crept into my consciousness and found a place in my heart. Expats, activists, and resisters awaiting travel visas while frequenting a fancy gin joint in French Morocco were what inspired me at a young age, the idea of wandering to lands far far away.

You'd think it would be a story easily lost on an eleven-year-old on the other side of the world in 1970s Brooklyn, but the film had me at "Hello Rick."

I wondered where they were. I asked, "Where is Morocco?" It was all strange in the most unfamiliar and intriguing way. Fez hats, hookahs, gambling, folks in love, and an airplane waiting to whisk Bogey and Bergman off is the stuff of Hollywood. However, the idea of escape to faraway lands caught my attention. The idea of skipping town and going somewhere touched me after that movie.

This Brooklyn girl never learned the fine art of driving. Having wheels in New York City is not only unnecessary, it is a burden, so I walk once I get unpacked in a new city or town. Feeling the ground beneath my feet centers and orients me. It helps me to find my way.

I'm attracted to the French idea of *la flâneur*; one who wanderers in a beautiful, poetic, and philosophical manner.

Walking can be a contemplative, spiritual, and aesthetic experience. The importance of a long journey is part pilgrimage, allowing the mind to clear. In that clearance, a peace arises. Inspired ideas have the space to come forward in answer to our deepest concerns.

What good is the drifter, the dharma bum? Does the monk or the poet have any value? What have writers and philosophers made of their walking, of their wandering?

The Poet Robert Frost was often asked while out walking if he was relaxing, having a break from writing? He'd say the walking part was the work. It was at those moments that his ideas came to him. He simply had to write down what was given to him while walking when he put pen to page.

Movement is a kind of salve for me. When I get lonely and afraid I ask myself, *Why can't I have a normal life?* Normal being a life with a family full of children. I adore children. Why can't I start a family and make a home instead of living a gypsy-like nomadic existence?

I have had many thoughts about what goes into having a family. I think of the immense effort of caring for and raising one's children. The house cleaning and food preparations, the education and guidance, the faithful need to be attentive and available are some of the things I would aspire to if I were to have a family.

While out walking one day I began to understand that though I miss not having children, I choose and prefer the freedom of movement, of flight, without worry. I am moved to wander. Spookily so, I wonder if I am called to wander.

I enjoy immensely quiet and solitude, travel and writing. These passions have profound drawbacks—for example, missing out on raising children or other paths not taken.

I have a romantic taste for walking. I walk to enjoy the beauty of this world. I walk to get in tune with the divine, with nature. I walk to be still and to know. I walk for the sheer joy of it.

As a wanderer, I witness the way the pleasures in life present themselves in every step. Sometimes—oftentimes— it is a quiet, unassuming mysterious welling up of beauty that surprises me, and getting lost while wandering is a part of it all as well.

I am beginning to wonder if it is me who has chosen the life of the wanderer, *la flâneur*. Or is it that the path of the wanderer has chosen me? I ponder these questions simply because when I drift through the winding, dusty, unfamiliar roads of Morocco, I feel more at home than ever. I encountered a sense of home long ago simply sitting beside my aunt watching *Casablanca* one Brooklyn evening. I haven't been the same since.

Laila

Saturday mornings are not necessarily the best day for a three-hour Spanish class. Maybe not the best for learning a new language. *La marcha* in Madrid for the most part ends just before sunrise. On three hours sleep I will myself to class.

The classroom fills quickly with students. Señor Hernandez arrives just at the top of the hour. The last student slips in and sits right next to me in the front row, in the seat closest to the door.

I am stunned. Left breathless. Class begins and I find it impossible to focus with her sitting beside me.

El professor introduces himself and asks us, the students, to do the same. My new neighbor, sitting beside me, introduces herself as Laila and says she is from Saudi Arabia.

My heart is pounding quickly, and I struggle for air finding it difficult to breathe. I have heard stories and seen pictures, but nothing has prepared me for what it actually feels like. Laila is dressed in black robes, covered nearly completely with only her eyes and hands visible. I glimpse her eyes peeking out from the open slit in her veil, and I watch her hands moving across the page of her notebook.

This is our first Spanish lesson. We are learning simple greetings and phrases, but I am distracted. I wonder where exactly Saudi Arabia is. I try to picture it on the map in my mind. I imagine spatial deserts and vast views of clear blue sky.

I have questions. *People actually live there?* I ask myself.

Laila leans in gently moving closer to me. She speaks in the softest whisper.

El professor looks at me and says, "Katherine, Laila *tiene una pregunta?*"

Una Pregunta. A question. Okay, who has a question? I ask myself. I'm incredibly confused.

Her soft whispers hidden behind her veil do not register with me. I am trying to wrap my mind around this moment. *It's . . . No . . . Could it be? It's Arabic. She's asking me a question in Arabic. Are you kidding me?* I ask myself.

"I . . . I don't speak Arabic," I inform the teacher.

"Try to understand her," he urges me.

Her tender fingers, astonishingly bare given that all else is veiled, are pointing to sentences on her page. I look into her eyes, I listen to the intonation of her voice, and I read the Spanish words on the page next to her notes handwritten in Arabic. I say something to the teacher. I don't know what comes out of my mouth, but I say something.

With illustrations on the chalk board and a few confusing hand gestures, *el professor* opens up Laila's question to the class, explaining it to us all.

And so this strange way of communicating becomes the custom for all our Spanish lessons together.

I arrive to class each Saturday morning dressed simply in shorts and T-shirt hastily thrown on after a quick shower and just a few hours' sleep after having danced the previous night away. The steamy summer Madrid days call for little covering. Bare arms and legs help keep one as cool as possible. *Madre mia.* But I'm here.

I feel like a tramp sitting next to Laila, who seems sweet and serene, veiled and wrapped in her black robes.

Laila's husband and children escort her to class each time. Her refined hands and the tender skin around her eyes reveal her youth. I imagine that she is quite young to be the mother of three.

I'm getting used to her gentle whispers and delicate movements with which she always greets me when she takes the seat next to mine.

Every time she has a question in class, she tries to communicate it to me. I do my best to decipher what she means, and I relay her question to the teacher. He then explains something to me in Spanish, and I repeat it to her to be sure we both understand these new lessons.

As time goes along and we learn more Spanish, I try to say some things to her in our new language. She looks into my eyes, watches my hand gestures as I attempt to share the information with her, and takes notes in her notebook in Arabic.

I learn in time that Laila's faith and culture disapprove of women speaking to men who are not relatives, so I, as a woman, have become the mediator between her and *el professor.* She speaks to me, and I bridge the gap that she cannot on her own. We all work it out and learn together with me in the middle.

I also come to understand that she is not to walk alone. She must be accompanied by her husband or a male family member. When each class ends her husband and children are always waiting for her just outside the classroom.

One day in class, something happens. I explain to Laila what the teacher has explained to me in answer to her question, and I can see the expression in her eyes change.

Did she just smile? Shit! She is smiling behind that veil! I muse to myself.

This is a revelation to me. I've gone so long without seeing her, this person who has been whispering to me from behind black robes for months, that to sense her smiling for the first time delights and moves me more than seeing her smile could have.

Laila and I develop an understanding, our own way of communicating. We lean in and whisper and giggle in a mix of a little bit of Spanish, her Arabic, and my English. El professor has to discipline us occasionally, gently—*una palabra es bastante* (a word is enough). It's the same for pupils around the entire world. We all know better, it's true. Whispers and giggling in class are disturbances. *Perdónanos.*

One day, after some months of Saturday lessons, we get to class and the teacher is not there. We all wait gathered in the hallway. The door to class is closed and locked. Maybe he's just running late, we all surmise.

Laila's husband can't wait any longer. He has to get to an appointment. He says a few words to her in Arabic and leaves with the children.

Shortly after, someone passing on the stairs inform us that there isn't class today. It's a holiday in Madrid.

In the midst of sighs from all the students, I'm not quite sure how, but it all comes together for me in an instant. While I'm standing on the stairs looking up at Laila who is a few steps above me, I grasp her predicament quickly. Her husband has just left with the children, there's no class today because of the holiday, and she is not to walk alone.

I take off with my books in hand down the stairs and out the building. Running through the Spanish plaza toward Laila's husband, I become self-conscious of the little shorts I'm wearing and a fitted summer halter.

"*Perdona! Perdona!*" I shout as I draw closer to Laila's husband and children who are walking through the plaza.

Reaching them I try to explain how there is no class today. I must have gotten enough of it correct in Spanish because he turns around with the children and they all start rushing back.

I run on ahead back to Laila and find her standing alone on the stairs in the hallway.

"*El viene ahora,*" I say. "Your husband is coming back now."

Her eyes tell me that she is smiling behind her veil, and this gets me again. I'm elated to see her eyes crinkle at the corners, and I know that besides her robes and veil she's also wearing a beaming smile.

Her husband and children rush back up the stairs, and I step back to leave Laila in the company of her family once again.

"*De nada,*" I say with easy fluency in response to Laila's husband's *thank yous.*

How do you say *"you are quite welcome" in Arabic*? I wonder. It's a pity I don't know more words in Arabic. I can say *assalamu alaikum* when wishing one peace. And my favorite, *inshallah:* we wish, we hope, we try . . . if God says so.

But then again, these sweet sentiments are a fine beginning.

Roma

Why Go?

"STAND HERE TO ACTIVATE YOUR SUPER POWERS" is what the street art encouraged. I walked across the white spray-painted sidewalk graffiti in Greenwich Village and wished that I could transport myself to Rome again. Indulge poetic dreams in a heady mix of haunting ruins. Visit the Vatican. Say a little prayer in Saint Peter's Basilica. Call out in the Colosseum. Spy on lovers kissing in Piazza Navona. Prance beneath streams of sunlight in the Pantheon. Sip Prosecco beside the Trevi Fountain.

Planning the Trip

It has been said that luck favors the prepared. In Rome's over crowded old town and narrow roads overflowing with tourists, it is wise to plan. Before you go, map out your dreams and desires, then arrive, relax, and go with the flow.

When to Go and Arriving in Rome

I did not do that. For me, the wheels touched down in Rome late at night—not the best time to arrive for a woman traveling alone per my experience. Daytime is the best time when the sun is high in the sky. It's easier to see the monsters then. I did not plan well. I did not plot a course or mark up a map. Not only was I unwise, I was quite stupid about it all. I thought I'd land and wing it, improvise and float along, fumble from Leonardo da Vinci–Fiumicino Airport and find my way to Piazza Navona.

Getting There and Away from Animal Encounters

"Taxi?"

"No thank you. But could you point me toward the train station. I'd like to take the train into the city center."

"The train station is closed," the taxi driver informed me to my surprise.

"It is?"

"Yes. I will take you to your hotel."

I assumed that that the train station would be open late. We are influenced by the environments in which we are raised. Not all public transportation systems around the world are open twenty-four a day like they are in New York City. I had never been to Italy. It was nighttime, and I didn't feel secure enough to figure out what to do in the dark in Rome.

"How much to the center of town?"

"Forty euro."

I didn't like the price, but what could I do? Plenty really, I thought to myself. If you fail to plan, then you plan to fail.

"Alright," I agreed.

"Just wait here. I'll be right back."

So I waited, watching the flux of people: sweethearts reuniting and families embracing as well as solo travelers finding their way through the crowds. It turned out that the taxi driver had a van in which he collected and transported a number of people to their hotels, dropping passengers off one at a time or in groups.

When we finally piled into his van, it was even later, and I was the only one traveling alone. He asked me to sit in the front seat. I climbed in and hoped that my hotel would be the first stop.

The last group to be dropped off was a family of three, and as the father of the family was getting out of the van, he gave me a strange look. Our eyes stayed fixed on one another for a moment, and he opened his mouth to say something, but he didn't. If you sense something, say something?

I began to hope that I'd be okay. I just needed to get to my hotel, and I needed to get there by midnight because that was the latest that my reservation would be honored. I hoped that I'd make it in time, and, more important, I hoped to make it safely.

There was a bad vibe in the air, so I made sure that the door where I was sitting in the front seat was unlocked, and even though it was chilly out, I rolled down the window just in case I needed to jump out or to scream in hopes that someone would hear me.

The taxi driver got back into the van and began speaking to me in Italian when he had been speaking to me, to all of us, in English before.

"Roll up the window!" He yelled at me, this time in English.

"I'd like some air. I'd like to leave the window open, please."

I lied. I wasn't sure if my fear was for a good reason or if it was all in my head. It was all the same to me.

He started yelling at me in Italian even though I couldn't understand him, and I screamed back at him demanding that he stop the van and let me out. He grabbed my leg, and I open the door of the van while it was moving. He shouted at me and slowed the van down, and I jumped out and insisted that he let me get my bags out of the back of the vehicle. I yelled at him with all the indignation I could call forth. I was scared shitless, but I didn't want him to know that.

"Give me my bags!" I screamed even louder.

"What's your problem?"

"Give me my fucking bags!" I shouted at the top of my voice while standing behind his van where my luggage was stored.

He jumped out of the driver's seat, walked to the back of the vehicle, and removed my bag from the trunk. I was happy that he didn't just drive off with my stuff.

I angrily handed him the cab fare. Silly, I know, but I was raised to believe that a deal is a deal. I should have understood that when men get nasty and aggressive, especially at night when all is dark and strange, all deals are off.

He let the cab fare fall to the ground, jumped back in his taxi, and sped off. I had no idea where I was. Wherever it was, it was dark and deserted. I began to walk in the dark with my suitcase, and I saw another man walking toward me on the otherwise empty street.

"Excuse me sir, do you know where I can find a taxi?" I asked, although I was still trembling with fear and anger.

He looked at me curiously as if he were wondering what was up, but he simply pointed ahead and said, "Keep walking straight, and you'll walk into a plaza. There you can find a taxi."

He spoke in English with an accent from home, from the States.

"Thank you, sir."

I followed his directions straight ahead until I reached a plaza, and there, just as he said, I found a taxi waiting.

I gave the name and address of my hotel to the driver, and he nodded as I climbed into the back seat of his taxi. I was leery and scared, but what else could I do in a deserted, unfamiliar place in the middle of the night? He circled the Plaza with its flowing and brightly lit water fountains, and we were off. Enchanting.

Soft jazz filled the air from the radio as we drove the narrow, dusty Roman roads. The driver barely said a word. In fact, he only spoke to let me know that my hotel was well known and that it was easy to get to. After the encounter with the first taxi driver, I blessed him silently. Seemed to me that his mamma raised him right. He pulled up in front of the hotel and jumped out to help me with my bag and wished me a goodnight.

It was nearly one in the morning—a three-hour ordeal. I wanted to tell the receptionist all about it but didn't.

"I'm sorry that I'm so late. I have a reservation."

"No worries, miss," the receptionist assured me. "You're fine."

When I found my way to my room, the crisp white sheets and soft cream-colored blanket on the bed were a soothing welcome. The color of the walls, painted in that terracotta hue that the Italians do so well, helped, too. The room was beautiful and easy on the eyes. I locked the door behind me and dropped my bags. I undressed, rinsed my face, brushed my teeth, then slid into bed—I was still shaken but starting to feel better. I said a prayer of thanks and asked for protection as I always do. Seems this prayer works.

Sights and Activities

With the new day's morning light shining in my room, I awoke with thoughts of the possibilities that lay ahead, with ideas of meandering through the historical city. I got out of bed, bathed, and dressed for the day with a mission in mind. This time I would map out a small plan, a short list for a day in Rome:

Piazza Navona
Trevi Fountain
Baths and Colosseum
Sistine Chapel
Spanish Steps
Saint Peter's Basilica
Pantheon

Before stepping outside the hotel, I thought to ask the receptionist for directions to the train station in order to go there first to buy a train ticket to Sorrento, my destination the next day.

"The train station is just across the street if you turn right at the corner," she informed me.

I looked at the receptionist in disbelief. "Across the street? So close?"

"Yes," she responded in her delicate, melodic Italian accent.

"And what time does the train station close?" I was curious.

"At midnight."

I was crushed by this answer considering my experiences the night before, but I didn't want the ordeal to be something to dwell on but, rather, something to learn from.

Arriving at the train station, I joined a line to buy a ticket from Rome to Sorrento.

These are the moments that a traveler has to herself, and she can use them to try to figure out how best to communicate what she wishes to say when she either doesn't speak the language or speaks it poorly. How can I best make myself understood? I have always heard Spanish and Italian people talk about how similar their two languages are. A Spanish person can understand what is written and said in Italian and vice versa.

My plan had been to use my Spanish in Italy. When I reached the clerk in the train station, there was a place for me to sit down in her little booth. *Bene.* In my experience, it is easier to speak a foreign language while sitting down. The more relaxed the body, the more relaxed the mind.

I asked to make a reservation *de Roma a Sorrento.* My Spanish seemed to work, and I had my tickets in just a few minutes. Before leaving, and just to be certain, I ask, *"A qué hora cierra la estación del tren?"*

"A mezzanotte," she confirmed, in Italian, the same answer that the hotel receptionist had told me.

"Bene. Gracie."

Rome in a Day

I rested on the Spanish Steps with a gelato. I had no idea it would be so crowded, and as a New Yorker, I know crowds. In New York, you learn Ninja-like ways when finding your way through crowds. I found a little spot on the steps and sat down in the sunlight hoping to finish my gelato before it melted. It was all deliciously coming to an end. I had just about completed my list of sights to see.

Suddenly, I had company. A young man sat beside me and said something in Italian. I had been so spooked by my previous encounter with the male Italian species that my ears closed up in their own involuntary defensive action and I couldn't hear a thing he said.

I reached nervously to touch the area of my body where I had placed my money holder to make sure that it was still safely where I had put it. I actually had fastened the thin little money belt around my waste and inside my panties. If someone were ever to get to it there, then I'd have more to worry about then the loss of money.

I ignored the man sitting beside me, but it didn't matter because he persisted, undeterred. *"Quel stress!"*

I stood up and cautiously moved through the people lining the steps. Empty spaces were hard to come by, but I found my way to another little spot, sat down again, and hoped for some peace this time.

I began to plan the next site to visit in Rome while I finished my gelato sitting there on the Spanish Steps, inspired by their beauty and number.

Getting Around and Money

I felt that it was important to see the Pantheon, the last item on my list, before leaving Rome the next day, even though I was quite exhausted from the days' wanderings. I could see quite easily on the map that it was near, but I needed to figure out how to walk there through the twists and turns of the old streets.

"Hello," I heard in an Italian accent, and I realized that I had company again.

Shit, shit, shit! I thought. It was the same guy. I ignored him, but he continued to speak to me in English.

"Are you on holiday? Are you enjoying yourself? Where are you from? Are you alone?"

I disregarded every single word. I said nothing and didn't even look at him. I remained sitting where I was this time in my coveted spot on the Spanish Steps and stared straight ahead while trying to enjoy the last little spoonfuls of my gelato.

Breathe . . . I continued to ignore him as he, undaunted, carried on his one-sided banter for about twenty minutes. The situation had surpassed absurdity, but it was also getting to be pretty funny in a way. He kept talking to me as if we really were having a conversation. Passersby, at first glance, would have thought that he and I were just two of the many people sitting side by side on the steps enjoying the weather and having a nice chat.

I tried to focus on my map again to find a route to the Pantheon even though I knew, with my poor directional sense, that it was unlikely to help. I would get lost anyway. I was exhausted from walking around Rome, but I couldn't leave without seeing the ancient Roman temple.

My buddy beside me continued to talk the entire time. "You know the Pantheon is beautiful. You must see it. I can show you where it is."

"Is it just over there?" I asked as I finally broke my silence and reacted to his latest comments. I spoke to him without looking in his direction.

"Yes, it's very close. I can show you."

"Just tell me where it is. Please."

As irritated as I was, my mom taught me to be respectful, which sometimes gets me into trouble, but I could almost hear her telling me, "Yeah, but I did not raise you to be a fool."

"It's near. You go this way, and then you go here," he explained to me while pointing and touching my map. Reading a map for me is like trying to read an unknown language. It's all Greek to me. It doesn't matter where I am; I'm directionally challenged no matter the language.

"I'll show you," he kept adding. "Let's go."

Reluctantly, I gave in. I stood up and, with a wave of my hand and weary spirit, signaled for him to lead the way.

"Do you mind if we stop for just a moment for granizado de café?" he said.

Every now and then, I rubbed the space below my belly where my money was tucked away inside my panties. It was still there.

"What is *granizado*," I asked, more annoyed than curious because we were supposed to be going to the Pantheon. What tricks does he have up his sleeve, I wondered as I took my first really good look at him. I noticed that he had pretty eyes.

55

"It's made by crushing cubes of frozen espresso coffee," he explained with his charming Italian accent.

I am not a coffee drinker, so I didn't see what the appeal of a coffee Icee was, and I'd just finished a cup of gelato, but since I was being stupid—and since I was in Rome after all—I said, "Okay, let's go for granizado."

I followed him around some turns in the narrow streets and off the beaten path to a little café full of Italians standing around, speaking energetically, and enjoying granizado.

"This is the best place in Roma for granizado," he said directly in my ear so that I could hear him over the din of the passionate conversations in the café.

I had to admit that it looked like he was telling the truth. The café was packed with cheerful patrons.

"Two?" he asked me as he prepared to place an order.

"Okay," I said again. Since I was already there and everyone seemed to be relishing the treats, I figured I should see for myself what all the fuss was about.

The granizado was sweet with a deep, full coffee taste. It was wonderfully indulgent. It disappeared quickly.

"Okay, let's go," he said, and we were on the move again through the winding streets.

As we walked, I slowly began to get that feeling a traveler can get when making her way in a foreign land when all the strange and beautiful places and spaces and faces and smells begin to sink in.

My guide talked incessantly. He told me that he was from Sicily and was a pharmacist in the military stationed in Rome. He had been a pharmacist in his little hometown in

Sicily, but he had been miserable because it was painfully boring there. He had thought that he had ruined his life, but he was deeply happy as a military pharmacist, and his life had changed for the better since he moved to Rome because he could wander all about the city each day after he was free from work.

He said he loved meeting people from other places, hearing their stories, and learning about their culture. "I love it," he beams with sheer joy.

He talked nonstop, but I began to enjoy it. It was not senseless talk without meaning. He was interesting, philosophical, and poetic.

"Here it is!" he said proudly when we reached the front of the Pantheon.

I stood there in awe of the sight and was captivated by my guide's enthusiasm and excitement as well. My guard was slipping. I thought that if he was after my money, then he was committed and dedicated and this was a clever, but time consuming, way of going about it.

The sun was beginning to set when we exited the Pantheon. It cast a golden light on the ending of a unforgettable experience.

"It really has been a beautiful afternoon," my guide said.

"Yes, it has been a sweet afternoon," I conceded, giving in again although I was still suspicious and wounded from my previous experience.

Eating
"Have dinner with me?" he asked.

So this was the reason for his kindness and attention. It was to get me to buy him dinner. This was how they work, I thought. My guard began to rise again. Then I said to myself that it would be worth it. I wouldn't mind buying him dinner to show my appreciation for the time and energy he had taken to show me around. I agreed to have dinner with him, and his smile, which hasn't vanished all day, widens.

"But first I must go home and change my clothes."

Aha! There it was. His plan had been to get me to go to his home all along.

"But you look fine. You look nice, actually," I said in an effort to avoid going with him to his apartment. But it was the truth, too. He did look good. There may be many things about Italian men that could piss one off, but fashion sense isn't one of them.

"What I am wearing isn't appropriate for dinner," he explained. "It's okay for strolling around in the afternoon, but not for dinner." He said, touching the fabric of his fine jeans and then the collar of his cotton shirt with sleeves rolled up to his elbows, "This particular blue worn with this kind of blue is not acceptable for dinner." I looked down at his soft Italian brown suede loafers as he offered his justifications. "Foreigners will never know the difference," he said with a kind of disgust at the idea. He added, emphatically, "But Italians—they know!"

I've never been one to stand in the way of cultural norms when I am traveling, and I tried to understand his reasoning. I acknowledged to myself that this was an Italian thing that I may never fully understand.

"Okay, so I'll wait for you." I said. "Where should we meet when you get back? And at what time?

"Why don't you come with me?"

"There's no way I'm coming with you."

"I know you have no reason to trust me, but I'll just go home and change into something proper for dinner, and we can enjoy a nice meal together before you leave Rome. I like your company. There's this really beautiful restaurant I want to take you to. It costs a little more, but it'll be worth it."

He had been teasing me all day about the fact that I hadn't tasted real Italian food yet and how it just wasn't right to visit Italy and not have a proper Italian meal.

"Let me introduce you to real Italian food."

"Alright. I will wait for you while you go and change for dinner."

He acquiesced to go home to change without me, and we agreed to meet back at the river in an hour.

He returned dressed in a light blue button-up shirt with the sleeves gently folded at his forearms, light tan summer wool trousers, and soft brown leather Italian lace-ups. I now could easily see the difference between hanging around the city in casual clothes and getting dressed for dinner. He had taught me an Italian fashion lesson.

Arts, Culture, and Philosophy

"I hope you will like this place. The food is quite special."

We walked along the river, turned into the old town, and found our way to a tiny restaurant just off a little plaza. It was full. Every seat inside and outside on the terrace was taken, and there was a line of people spilling out onto the sidewalk patiently waiting with drinks in hand and lost in conversation.

"I knew it would be crowded, but we had to try," my guide said.

He spotted the owner and asked in Italian what the possibility was of getting in. He said, "The owner says that he will get us in, but we have to wait a little bit, so let's go have a coffee, and we'll come back."

It was already nearly 10:00 p.m. I understood that late dinners were normal in Italy, especially on summer Friday nights, but I still needed to get back to my hotel, and I was worried about traveling alone again late at night. I did my best to dismiss my apprehension and decided I would take my chances with a taxi again and enjoy this evening, my last one in Rome.

Walking along the river's edge, we took a road that bent toward Campo de' Fiori, the plaza with a statue of the philosopher Bruno who was burned at the stake for heresy. My guide looked at me and said, emphatically, "You would burn! If you lived during the time of Bruno, you, too, would burn."

I was a bit shaken by this declaration, but then I realized that it was profound praise to be thought of in the same breath as Bruno. All this time, all during this day, I had been obsessing about this talkative stranger, wondering if he was a risk to my safety or, rather, a kindred spirit and ally in my quest and desire for cultural and intellectual enrichment. Now he was equating me with the great philosopher and truth-seeker who upset the status quo and was a threat to conventionality, to orthodoxy. To be held in this light was a compliment.

To pass the time while we waited for a table for dinner, for the proper Italian meal that my guide had promised and not common touristy fair, we stopped for coffee at an outdoor café and savored the moment by watching the weekend crowd of elegant people pass through the square. We sat and took the opportunity to talk some more, to keep company a little longer.

Eating and Drinking

Checking the time, my guide suggested we head back. "Let's go eat."

We returned in perfect time and the owner showed us to a table in the back of the restaurant. The place was simply adorned and had a cozy, sincere atmosphere.

"The wine selection here is wonderful," my guide said. "They really know their wine."

He selected a red wine for both of us, but not before asking me a series of questions in order to ascertain my tastes. He also chose several small plates from the Italian menu. When they arrived and were placed before us, they took up the entire table.

We enjoyed the delicate feast as we sat together at the table filled with carefully prepared dishes and delicious red wine. We talked for hours sharing stories of our lives, hopes, and dreams, our disappointments as well as our accomplishments. We recounted our experiences of the day and our love for travel and adventure.

No one disturbed us. The waiters only checked in from time to time to refill our wine glasses and serve desert and espresso, and then they were off to attend to other guests. We sat there and talked and laughed for hours while time slipped by and the happenings around us in the restaurant went unnoticed.

We finally realized that the restaurant was preparing to close, so we requested the check. It had been such a lovely evening that by this time, I thought that it would be my pleasure to pay for dinner.

He asked me to wait to see if he had enough cash to pay the bill. It was silly, I thought, that he would even think of doing that. I argued that paying for dinner would be my small contribution for such a beautiful day. He insisted and paid the entire bill, which turned out to be quite expensive, though it was worth every cent.

"I'll drive you back to your hotel."

"I don't think that's a good idea."

"Don't be silly. Of course, I will take you to your hotel."

It was late, and I wasn't quite sure what the best decision was. Despite the fact that he had been a gentleman the entire day up to that point, I still had some apprehension—tiny as it may have been—lingering deep within me. I considered his offer and, given the late hour, agreed to let him drive me.

Relief and Rhythms

Sitting in the passenger seat, I began to realize how tired I was from the long day of walking around Rome. If I had closed my eyes, I would have fallen asleep in seconds. He turned on some music and lowered the window. The cool air blowing in and Andrea Bocelli's voice helped to keep my sleepiness at bay. As we traveled down the Roman roads in the wee hours, I felt so good, so comfortable—as if we were being transported on the wings of the beauty of the day. I knew that my soul had been touched so gorgeously by this experience.

It was two in the morning when he pulled up in front of my hotel.

"What time does your train depart?"

"It's at nine in the morning from Rome to Sorrento. I'm going to meet my friends there."

"You'll love it. It's so beautiful there, with the cliffs that hang over the sea, the fantastic colors. Let me know how you like it."

"I will," I promised.

He wrote down his telephone number and email address.

"Write me when you're back in the States."

Exhausted, I found my way up to my hotel room. I slept for only a few hours before checking out of the hotel and catching the train to Sorrento. I arrived there just in time to meet my friends for lunch.

Sitges

I have visited Barcelona several times, but I'm often at a loss when friends ask for tips on things to see when in Barcelona. I find it strange that I have not come up with anything to suggest. All the travel books clearly lay out the must-sees when visiting the city, so I would not be sharing anything new by suggesting a visit to, for example, the stunning Sagrada Família.

When I visit a place, I do so in an organic manner. I never know exactly what I'm going to do. I just let the experiences come as they may. As a result, it's difficult for me to say to someone, "You should see this."

I mostly feel my way around when I arrive somewhere new, tuning into what my heart tells me when I wake up in the morning, but I may have figured something out. I like to tell stories, so I have thought about some of my favorite memories and am beginning to get a few ideas to share. You see, It doesn't make sense to say, "You should visit the Mediterranean sunset." But I can tell the story about the most beautiful sunset I have ever seen.

Friends invited me for an evening in Sitges, a town that I had never heard of. They said it was absolutely beautiful there. It's just outside of Barcelona. We took the train out. When we arrived, the sun was just beginning to set. We walked along the sea taking in the breathtaking beauty of the small seaside town in its pre-twilight glory.

In Sitges, you can visit a *feeling,* experience the sensation of walking along the sea with friends and loved ones, enjoy conversations and companionship amid the awe-inspiring beauty of the place.

If you are patient, a moment will come when you can witness the sun set when it seems to be the closest to the earth it has ever been and it is its most golden—golden with hints of red and purple. Beauty that grand can cause ones heart to skip a beat as the sun slips down below the horizon. Afterward, lingering rays of light will continue to illuminate the skyline and inspire your imagination.

I suppose it was necessary for me to express that memory—to get it out of my system—in order to be able to share other thoughts about Barcelona. This has created the essential space to remember the endless wonders there, like the fun, fantastical, colorful playland of Parc Güell and the stunning architecture along Barcelona's grand boulevards.

And in Catalonia, you will find yourself drinking less of Spain's delicious red wine and sipping a bit more Cava, Spain's own luscious sparkling wine. It's all coming back to me now. I might have a few things to share . . .

On Love

On a hot summer's afternoon, I ran into the house for a cool drink and a quick break from an intense double Dutch session. The spinning ropes and rhythmic skipping left me parched.

While standing in the kitchen, I thought I'd let my mom in on a rumor I had just heard the kids talking about outside. Standing beside her sipping sweetened homemade lemonade, I interrupted her cooking and leaned in to whisper that Jodi, her best friend, was gay—that she was a lesbian and had a *girlfriend*.

I was filled with the spirit of gossip from the playground, even though at seven years old I did not fully understand what being gay meant.

Mom casually looked at me and said, "How nice it must be to have someone to love."

I considered what she said and was moved by the tenderness in her voice. *It's true, how nice*, I thought, and I ran back out to play.

Jillian Was Here

Her silence is a kind of secret when it comes to Jillian. Her husband would object, of course. How do you not leave out a thing like this? A secret is this important. She often thinks of Jillian, her first love, when she sees her wedding rings in the crystal dish on the marble counter top in the bathroom.

This morning after a soothing shower she remembers all over again why she loves these moments on Sunday mornings when the whole day is ahead of her. All responsibilities and chores are tended to the other six days of the week. Sundays are hers to do just as she pleases, to take time to rest from all the things that normally call for her attention. These moments are a kind of personal sabbath for her.

She wrapped herself cozily inside a plush pink towel allowing it to soak in the remaining moisture while thoughts of Jillian filled her mind. She was accustomed to these gentle intrusions, these memories resurfacing in the private moments of her life. There seemed to be nothing she could do about them except to make friends with them.

Her eyes glimpsed again the thin platinum and diamond wedding set in the crystal dish on the counter. Jillian had accompanied her to pick up the wedding bands days before the ceremony. When her ring was placed on the glass display case, the sales assistant had mistaken Jillian for the bride to be, and before either of the women could say anything, the sales assistant had reached for Jillian's hand and had slipped the ring onto her long, smooth finger to test the sizing.

She saw Jillian panic in the way that she did at the mere mention or idea of commitment. *I did ask her to marry me,* she consoles herself, remembering with a twinge of regret Jillian's gentle refusal.

Love doesn't have to run both ways in order for it to be real. She thinks of Jillian still, a cherished companion if only in her memory. Standing in front of the bathroom mirror, she lifts the rings from the dish and puts them on again.

Is it so that life is always right? She wonders. *It could be,* she thinks. Her two precious girls are clambering on the other side of the door calling for her to hurry up. Sunday family outings, which entail ice cream, always need to happen as soon as humanly possible.

It would have been different with Jillian, but who's to say better? She reasons with herself. Her love for her was simple and easy—like this Sunday morning, a sabbath where one can simply *be* with no exertion.

She is happy, though what she wanted with Jillian gets her to wondering how different her life might have been. She recalls the love she felt so long ago, the whispers and coy smiles, the notions of stillness and quiet between lovers. On tranquil mornings like this, she can almost feel, like a scar, the inner scripture unconsciously tagged on her heart all those years before: *Jillian was here.*

Spy Games

The downstairs door clicked as it unlocked. Sibley pushed it open and stepped inside. She gripped the wrought iron handrails on the spiral staircase to guard against slipping as she went up the stairs, one step after the other toward the end. Letting go requires steadiness and courage.

The door of Hassan's apartment was slightly ajar and Sibley stepped in, knowing it was for the last time.

She was able to detect the aroma of chocolate chip cookies baking in the kitchen. The enticing scent filled Hassan's home and mingled with the lyrics of the song "Until" on the stereo. She would recognize Cassandra Wilson's sultry jazz voice, full and warm, anywhere, a voice that soothes and flows as smoothly as warm molasses. The lyrics were slow and comforting. Good for letting go.

Stepping out of her sandals, Sibley's bare feet sunk into the plush gray-white carpeting that covered Hassan's entire home except the kitchen. She folded her white silk summer dress between her long legs and collapsed into a deep corner of the sofa. She was in heaven whenever she was near him. This time she reminded herself simply to breathe, to take deep breaths.

From her seat, she scanned the living room as she often did and gazed upon the bookshelves overflowing with the most tempting titles. She caressed the collection of vintage book spines with her glances, touching, in her mind, the pages with her adoration of literature. In the far corner beside the bookshelves, she spotted his unpacked luggage fresh from his return flight from Egypt.

"Yes, I'm inside!" Sibley answered Hassan's warm welcome coming from the kitchen. She was desperate to steal a few more moments to herself to indulge in the sweet sensation of his home and his nearness.

She could hear him moving around the kitchen, the origin of the yummy scents that drifted in on her daydreaming. The auburn and ginger colored hints of sunlight bled in through the floor-to-ceiling windows as the day's light began to fade.

"What are you thinking about?" She hadn't heard Hassan enter the room. He slid in beside her on the sofa. He was wearing his cozy grey sweats and white cotton T-shirt, and he tangled his legs and bare feet up with hers.

He's too pretty for a man, she thought to herself. *His beauty is stunning.* His big pools of brown eyes and soft tanned skin melted most hearts easily. His was a beauty that gently commanded a speechless appreciation. While playfully running her fingers through his soft fluffy curls, she giggled to herself because of the message on his T-shirt: bad hair day.

"I love you *too* much," he said as he often did. "Why do I have to work so hard to see you? You've got me wrapped around your finger, and I'm not proud of it," he teased her, pouting and pretending to be angry.

"Are you baking cookies? Oh, my goodness, they smell delicious!" Sibley intentionally changed the conversation, even though she greedily wanted to know.

"It's a surprise! Can you guess what kind?" he asked as he untangled himself from her and hopped off the sofa to rush back into the kitchen.

She followed him into the kitchen and stood behind him to look over his shoulder as he pulled the cookies from the oven. She had to hold back her tears from the knowledge that she had to leave him without so much as a goodbye.

She wasn't allowed to tell him the truth that a new assignment called her elsewhere and that she had to leave tomorrow. The words would have been too painful and would have gotten stuck in her throat anyway.

Her report, in regards to Hassan, was: *There's nothing to see here.* Only that she fooled around and fell in love and that Muslims make chocolate chip cookies, too.

Touch

"I love you too momma. Ok, *adiós.*"

Giselle touches the screen of her iPhone to end the call. All of her family and the warm sunny beaches of Mallorca are a long way away from the Manhattan ballet studio she finds herself in this Sunday morning.

Lifting herself from the floor, she positions herself once again. Lifting her torso, allowing her feet to face forward parallel beside one another, she begins gently to raise her right foot. Alternating each foot. Raising and lowering her heels. Keeping her knees soft. Making absolutely sure she rolls through her entire foot.

Again, lifting her torso upright . . . *Uff! There it is again,* she thinks to herself.

A sharp pain runs down the left side of her neck. The pain is awful and nearly unbearable when it presents itself.

I can't practice like this. I can't dance like this, she reasons with herself.

Giving in to a colleague's advice she will go to her physical therapist appointment early.

It's true, dancers live with pain. Bruised ribs and aching feet. Tender muscles.

Still, this pain in her neck and shoulder she's unable to bear any longer.

She thought to not tell her mother. It would only cause her to worry which is the worst when one is so far away and unable to help.

She's been able to make it through her performances but not without pain. And now the pain is unbearable.

It started as a strange feeling in her shoulder. She thought she'd slept wrong or something and it would straighten itself out. But it hasn't. First it seemed to spread down her arm and now it's moving up along her neck causing unbearable headaches.

The human body is indeed a perfect machine the way each bone, muscle, and fiber is connected. One thing out of sorts can affect a whole range of movement.

Giselle grabs her sweater and wraps it around her waist. It's no way to walk through the streets of New York City in dance shoes and a lavender leotard, powder pink tights and woolen leg warmers. Or perhaps New York City might be the only place in the world where a lady, or a gentleman, can walk out like that and no one blinks an eye.

She'll go right now. Walk over to St. Luke's Roosevelt.

Besides this one scheduled appointment, today was supposed to be an easy day off. A bit of stretching. A simple easy run through her routine on her own, and then she planned to spend the rest of the day quietly, quiet as humanly possible before her evening performance.

She could use some silence in the midst of the noise and busyness of the Upper West Side.

To get away—from the traffic and crowds, horns and sirens, the aggression of shoppers consuming, and the heartbreak of being unable to help the homeless, asking for spar change, who haven't enough—will ease her heart.

The show is coming to its end, and it will do her some good to get back home to her mother's cooking, the warm sandy beaches of *Palma,* and all who she loves.

Taking a seat in the back of the waiting room after signing in, she is hoping this doesn't take forever. *Por favor no tarde mucho* is her silent request. Her whispered words floating quietly in the air of the room.

She finds a seat in the corner of the room and turns sideways in the seat in an attempt to relax about it all.

Only moments later, the cutest little toddler walks unsteadily over to her. Giselle lifts her head and looks around for the little one's mother.

"Where's your momma baby?" she asks gently as he is now reaching up trying to crawl into her lap.

How strange, she thinks.

She lifts him in her arms while standing to look over the few people in the emergency room for one who might be his mother.

Her heart begins to beat fast and she asks "Where's your momma sweetie?"

Rubbing her finger along his chubby little cheeks he gets comfortable in her arms. His pudgy little fingers touch her face as well. It's unusual to be so close to a baby she does not know. She's aware that people are seriously guarded about their children.

The other thing is, as she's thought about this before, mommies tend to have a club, a mommy's club. At least in New York City. As a single girl in the city without children, spending time around babies is supremely rare.

She immediately feels how soft and warm and comforting this little one is in her arms as he touches her face. The feeling is soothing and he smells good; a soft baby-powderish scent she can detect in his nearness.

A girl can go a long time easily without relating to anyone in New York City. It's a tough town. People keep to their tiny spaces avoiding all forms of any real contact or connection. People barely even look at one another. No eye contact is an unwritten rule.

She marvels at how New Yorkers can position themselves on the most crowded subway cars, holding their positions, and in a sense still not come close to one another. It's an existence alien to her everyday life back in Spain.

She realizes he's stealing her heart, this little one, as she's walking over to the receptionist unaware of the relaxing of her body. A comforting relief, easing the tensions within her. Even the pain in her neck and shoulder begins to lessen.

"Excuse me miss, ummm, this baby, it's not my baby. He just kind of wandered over to me. I don't know where his mother is."

"I'm sorry?"

"This little boy came over to me. He's not mine. I don't know who the mother . . ."

"There! There he is! How did you get in here?" Out of breath, a woman lifted the baby from Giselle's grasp.

Giselle could feel the warmth going out of her arms.

The toddler's mother looked at Giselle curiously standing in the waiting room in her dance gear

"Umm. I'm not sure which way he came from. I looked up and he was suddenly crawling into my lap.

"I'm so sorry." The mother apologized. "I was getting dressed after speaking with the doctor and I looked up and he was gone! He's just learning to walk, but he can get away so quickly. I can't believe this has happened."

Giselle smiled and wiggled the fingers of the little one and was in the midst of her goodbyes to the toddler when the receptionist informed her, "Ms. Elias, the physical therapist will see you now."

Giselle explained to the physical therapist about the excruciating aching in her neck and shoulders and the unbearable headaches while he, on the other side of the room, leaned over the sink washing his hands in soapy water.

Drying them he began to examine her placing his warm fingers along her neck, down her shoulders, and across her back, then along her arms.

His hands, his touch, felt good to her and at the same time she thought once again of the little boy who had come to her in the emergency room. The toddler's coos and soft, warm little body and baby scent against her chest and his arms around her shoulders had been comforting.

Her thoughts were interrupted by the ring of her cell phone. Having a quick look at the screen of her phone nearby, she quickly reached for it.

"*Perdoname?* It's my mother!" Giselle abruptly touches the screen to receive the call.

Her hair, which was only loosely pinned up, falls down along her shoulders. Before the therapist could lift his hands from examining her shoulders her hair fell into his hands and spills through his fingers.

"*Sí mama*. Ok." Giselle touches the screen of her phone once again and ends the call.

"I'm so sorry. It's just that my mother is so far away. I hate to miss her call when she rings. I worry."

"Where are you from?" he asks while glancing over her chart again.

"You see? I hate it when people ask me this question. I think my English is getting perfect and people can tell I am from somewhere else."

He smiles and reminds her, "Almost everyone in New York City is from somewhere else."

"It says here you dance. You dance for the American Ballet Theatre?"

"Dancing is a sweet job. That's what Fred Astaire says," she shares with him as she is mindful of this privilege of her work.

"So how does one become a prima ballerina?"

"We're talking about practice. An immeasurable amount of practice," she lets him know with a shy smile, thoughts coming to her mind of how she runs with seemingly boneless contortionists performing breathtakingly magnificent maneuvers. She loves it.

"Let's see what we can do to get you back on the job." The physical therapist was easy on the eyes, and his warm smile touched her heart. She felt less alone for a moment.

You Can Touch My Hair
A Sunday Ritual

If you come visit me on Sunday, we can play after I get my hair done. You can touch my hair—I don't mind, but that's just me. A lotta people don't like that 'cause you don't just let anybody touch you. It's that personal, that's all. Be respectful, momma says, and be respected.

It's the curliness that makes my hair soft and fluffy. Feel how soft it is? It's not tough as it seems. None of us are, momma says.

When my momma washes my hair in the kitchen sink, it feels good. Soothing. That's a new word that I just learned, soothing.

She used to lay me on the counter space beside the sink and hold my head in her hand and dip my hair beneath the faucet to shampoo it. I'm tall enough now, so I can stand at the sink while she washes my hair.

She just suds it up with shampoo and rinses it out before she puts in the conditioner. I'm tender headed, so she starts at the ends of the curls and takes it easy. She combs the conditioner gently through my hair to get the tangles out.

The conditioner always drips down my face, but I just wipe it away from my eyes with my fingers. I tell momma it tickles and it's warm and watery. Momma says she knows 'cause her momma did the same thing for her on Sunday afternoons.

Then she rinses out the conditioner and wraps my hair up in a towel. It's usually warm and soft, fresh from the laundry momma did in the morning.

So for the last part, I gotta sit on the floor so that when mom sits on the sofa I'm between her legs. She puts this light oil in my hair. Feel it. It's soft and it smells good. It's got vanilla in it. Then she braids it or puts it into Afro puffs. I like it when she gives me a part off the center or tilted ponytails.

When my auntie comes by on weekends before I get my hair done and it's all puffy and wild on top of my head, she just looks at me and smiles and says, "Sometimes you just gotta sit at home with your hair all messed up." That can feel good, too.

Lip Gloss Is for Beginners

Sweet Sixteen, Seventeen, and Eighteen in their T-shirts and summer shorts, the girls in my neighborhood were lovely, and I wanted to be pretty just like them. And even more than that, I absolutely adored the pink shimmering lip gloss on their lips. The lip gloss even looked like it tasted good, like sweet cotton candy on a summer afternoon in Brooklyn.

The summer of my seventh birthday, I stood in the kitchen of our home, and I asked my mother if I could have some pink lip gloss like the girls outside were wearing. I simply said, "Mom, I want some lip gloss like Sharon and 'em have on."

She looked at me curiously and gently explained, "Baby, those girls are older than you. They're teenagers. Lip gloss and lipstick are for big girls and ladies. Wait a while and you'll be able to wear it when you're older."

I begged her. "Mom, pleeeease," but her no meant no, and there was no changing her mind.

So I had to think of another way to get the pretty, sweet gloss that I longed for. I talked about it with my friends, and a few of them were sympathetic to my plight and vowed to help me get some lip gloss. They even could picture themselves wearing a little taste of it themselves.

We came up with the idea of going to our neighborhood five-and-dime to steal just one off the shelf. We didn't need more than one. We could share it. And it would just be this one time. We girls all agreed on this plan.

We marched into the store on a mission, and I lifted the lip gloss off its hook. My friends gathered around to shield me as I hid it in the pocket of my shorts. We headed for the door, and my heart was beating fast. I could already see it— finally, we would have our glossy, shimmering lips.

Just before stepping outside the door, we were called to come back into the store by a security guard, but to us seven-year-olds he looked like a police officer. In his official-looking uniform, the difference was lost on us. He stood before us and told us to come with him. His height was looming and his uniform intimidating. We girls locked hands with one another and followed the officer. He took us to the back of the store and put us in a small, bare room with only tables and chairs. He closed the door once we were inside and told us to sit down.

Who knows what he said. My heart was beating so fast, and I was filled with such fear that I couldn't concentrate. I asked him if we could have our one phone call. I had watched enough cop shows to know we were supposed to get one phone call. My mom was going to be angry with me, but it would be better than going to jail like I had seen on television.

The officer let us know we would be in jail over the weekend and we probably wouldn't get out until later in the week after we saw the judge on Monday.

I actually fell out of my chair onto the floor. Crawling up from the floor I found support along a wall. I tried to steady myself from this news.

A second officer came into the room and saw us girls gathered there, and the first officer caught him up on what we had done. The second officer studied us for a moment and let out a deep sigh. Breaking the tense, tear-filled silence he said to his partner, "Well, perhaps we could consider forgetting all about this and letting these girls go?"

The first officer considered this benevolent suggestion. We girls were terrified and in hysterics, and we hung on his hesitation—we would only be able to catch our breath if he agreed with the second officer to let us go. Only after we acknowledged that we understood that stealing was wrong and that we wouldn't do it again did he set us free.

My friends ran out of the room in tears. I followed slowly and looked back just for a moment with regret at the lip gloss that I had left on the table. I can still see it in my mind after all these years, the lip gloss lying there on the table as we left the room. With heavy hearts and in no hurry we walked home together holding hands, tears still running down our cheeks.

When I got home, I still could not let the matter go and came up with a new plan. I made up a lie and told my mother that I had gone to the five and dime with Teresa, who was one of my best friends, so that she could buy lip gloss with money that her mother had given her. I added, "After Teresa bought it and when we were leavin', the officer thought that we hadn't paid for it and took it away—and now we ain't got her lip gloss that her mother paid for!"

Mom could be gentle, but if you wronged her or crossed any lines, get out of the way. I knew this, and anyone who knew my mother knew this, so I thought that she would help to get the lip gloss back.

She never questioned me when I told her something. She just searched my eyes and trusted me. She always trusted me. I had never given her reason not to trust me. She grabbed me by the hand, and we almost flew out the door. She was angry. No one was going to cheat or be unfair to her child.

My little, narrow legs could barely keep up with her long, quick strides. Somehow, I still had time to think before reaching the store about what would happen when we got there and the officer told my mom what actually happened. I knew that I'd be in big trouble.

Looking up at her and trying to keep pace as we raced down the block in her haste to right the wrong that she thought had been done to her child, it pained me to open my mouth.

"Um, mom? See—"

She was still moving fast.

"Um, I have to tell you something."

She came to an abrupt halt, and looked me in the eyes and waited.

"I, um. See, we—"

She waited some more.

"See, me and Teresa and Shani went to the store to get the lip gloss. But we didn't really have any money, so the truth is we stole it."

I waited for what seemed like an eternity for her to say something. Instead of the anger that I was sure would follow, she looked at me incredulously.

"What is it with you and this lip gloss?" she asked.

I couldn't explain it to her. I didn't have the words—I was only seven. I had no answer that would appease her. All

I could do was shrug my shoulders and think to myself, It's shiny and pink. What more can I say? What more needs to be said? I felt even more.

She turned around on her heels and marched back home dragging me with her and reprimanding me all the way. In all honesty, I don't remember any of the speech she made. I heard none of it. I only had that lip gloss—there on the table in the bare room in the store where I had left it— on my mind.

For the rest of that summer I watched the pretty teenage girls on my block and obsessed about what they were wearing. I listened to what they talked about, and, of course, I dreamed of the lip gloss they were so lucky to have.

For more years after that when the weather warmed and, as my southern raised mom says, "as the sap rises," I'd see the older girls perfumed and pretty, and I longed so much to be like them.

I was fourteen, seven years later, when my mom gave me permission to wear *a little lip gloss and some eyeliner*, as she put it, like the other girls in my high school.

A year later, at fifteen, I kissed a boy for the first time. I pursed my lips and we kissed. The lip gloss I was wearing was sticky and just got in the way.

How to Spend It

"Whatever happened to the forty-hour work week? That's respectable, isn't it? I'm just saying sixty hours is too much." Anthony stated his case.

Ashley responded as she wiggled her feet in the clear Caribbean waters while sitting seaside in her powder pink bikini. "What are you talking about? There have been a million studies. People in western countries are the most productive and have the strongest economies because of hard work. I mean look at the atmosphere here. Everything is super slow and relaxed.

"Back home we are working and getting things done. That's why the world admires the United States and our standard of living. So many people want to come to our country."

Anthony wasn't sure if it was a discussion worth having. He didn't think he could get her to understand his way of seeing things. He decided to give it one more shot.

"I disagree. I don't know where you come up with these ideas. And what's the point of working such long hours?"

"That's a stupid question," Ashley thought and said so.

"Ok, indulge me. Humor me."

"What?"

"Why work so much?"

"It's what we do. A good work ethic is decent. Plus, I plan to enjoy a nice lifestyle. Like I want to be poor and always worrying about money?"

"But having a lot of money has nothing to do with being content in life."

Ashley was getting annoyed and seeing more and more that Anthony could never be the guy for her. She tried to further explain herself.

"Maybe I'm not talking about being rich," Ashley said. I'm just talking about enjoying a nice lifestyle. What's wrong with that?"

"Nothing. It's just that you equate working long hours and having things as the reason for living, the ultimate goal. I don't know if that equation makes sense. The way I see it, the point of you working sixty hours a week is to be able to enjoy nice things, to be able to get away to luxurious vacations, to buy and live in an expensive house that you have no time to be in anyway! Is there something commendable to be said for people who live their lives at a slower pace, enjoying a relaxed way of life, daily sea baths, if they want? Does that make them un-productive?"

"This is ridiculous. I just appreciate working a little so I can have a little more."

"I agree with you completely. I'm only saying it could be worth it to have a look at what we are doing as a nation—and even as a couple. We are constantly working, which means less time to take care of ourselves and our relationship."

Ashley thought that Anthony might have a point, but she was so worked up she wasn't willing to admit it.

"Let's just drop it. This is going nowhere. Anyway, let's go and prepare ourselves for our tee time?"

In the hotel room Ashley busied herself getting dressed for golf, far too annoyed to speak to Anthony any further about the topic.

After a few holes on the golf course, she had an idea. She thought to ask the caddy. He had been born and raised in Barbados, and the saying written across his chest on his T -shirt caught her eye: *"100% Bajan. Just add rum."*

"Excuse me sir, just out of curiosity, how many hours do you work a day?"

Anthony could not believe his ears. He wanted to disappear right on the spot. *Who does that?* He thought to himself and walked away toward the pro shop in frustration.

The caddy answered easily, without a problem, "Six hours. I mean, I'm not on the course every day for six hours, but between my other responsibilities, it comes to about six hours."

"You work six hours a day, that's it? How do you live like that?"

The caddy threw the question back to Ashley.

"Well how many hours a week do you work, if I may ask,"

"Sometimes sixty."

"And I imagine you dream all year of getting away from it all? To come to a place like this where I live and sit on the beach for two weeks out of the year?" Then the caddy added, "How do *you* live like that?"

The Lost Ones

I can imagine his loneliness living in a world without the proper guidance of loved ones. I think of him often. I don't know much about depression, but I understand that people self-medicate, to make what hurts go away. I'm not sure if the pain is why he started drinking. I think we were too young to understand the pain we were in, or to even feel it—just like a child doesn't feel the cold when she is playing in the snow. It's one of youth's precious gifts. We don't feel what can be painful—or its underlying effects—as deeply until we are older.

I think he started drinking because alcohol was so readily available to him. That's a hole many people fell into in our neighborhood. Being so young, I believe he didn't have the ability to discern the roads down which his actions might take him.

I imagine his has been a life of emptiness and loneliness and *lostness,* the human attempt to find the way and fill the void. I don't know this for sure because I haven't spoken to him for more than ten years now, my neighbor, my friend that is. But I've heard stories.

I get to thinking sometimes that the things that haunt him run deeper and are more devastating to him than my own demons are to me. I think the difference between us is that I had some resources and he had none in our efforts to escape the demons of our neighborhood.

I grew up in a loving home. I also had teachers who gave their time to me because they sensed my love of learning; storybooks to keep me company and spur my imagination; and some kind of inner impulse, an unconscious self-preservation, that moved me to visit a friend's house often in search of companionship.

He was full of energy and the need to explore. If not guided in the right direction, in a harmful environment, that energy can lead to destruction. Use your power for good, as the saying goes, but with little or no guidance, coupled with less love, his energy led him to look for kinship in more damaging places. Where I found solace and safety in the company of friends, he found something else entirely different.

Our immediate community was filled with violence and drugs, so he only had to step out of the door into it, literally. But he found a community there, a group of boys who could run together. He didn't have to be lonely at home anymore. He didn't have to be heartbroken alone, which lessoned his pain somehow, one would think.

Many people don't like him. He is angry and disrespectful, they say. You would be too, probably, if no one took the time to love you, if no one took the time to care for you. I was there. I saw what happened. It has been a lifetime for him of being on his own, making mistakes, and suffering. How do you get it right when you have no idea what right looks like or feels like?

I think of him often. I haven't been around him, or anyone else really from the old 'hood. I've been trying to save myself from the demons of our past. Today I got to thinking, *what do we do with the stuff that haunts us?*

My own "high" of choice has been movement. I move to breathe, to forget loneliness and emptiness, and to see beauty. The ghosts stay away as long as I stay in motion.

But now I'm tired, and I'm better. Running has its way of burning away that which is not needed, that which is not useful. And I find myself still, still as in quiet and more at peace.

He's better, too, my childhood neighbor and friend. He's kicked the drinking, I hear. If you've ever had a deep, debilitating pain that's been reduced to a whisper of what it was, I tell you, a quiet relief moves within.

These days, though, I still move and travel, more for pleasure than desperation, I wake up in the mornings, and I wonder *where do I go from here?* And I think of all who are lost, and I silently send love for healing, for we have all been like partners in crime, on the run, who separated long ago to improve our chances for escape. We always keep each other in mind along our way, and we hope that all the others are surviving and are alright.

Karma

Tell her this is what to do. Make sure she gets his social security number. She has to. Don't forget.

God ain't gon' bless him. You don't do that!

How old is the baby? Three months? She might have to wait a few more months. She'll have to find a job, and then she can afford a nursery.

If he wants to be like that, go ahead. You can't just walk away from your responsibilities like that. A judge will be sure to make him support his baby. They take the money out of your pay now, straight away. She'll be okay. It's going to take some time. But if he wants to walk away from his marriage just because he wants his old life back, the judge will be sure he pays his share for taking care of the baby.

His life ain't gon' be the same anyway. He thinks he can just go back to hanging out and partying all the time? He has obligations now.

What about her family? Can they help her? Oh, everyone is in Connecticut? She's all alone in Brooklyn? Oh, that's too bad.

Me? Your father and I were so young when we had y'all. I would be at home cooking and cleaning and taking care of you all, and he would come in at the end of the day hitting on me. I couldn't take it anymore. He came home one day, and we were gone.

I said as long as I can carry my babies, they're coming with me, all three of you. Ma put us on a bus in Fort Lauderdale and we rode the bus to New York City. It was alright. Auntie Josephine and Uncle Norris helped us once we got to Brooklyn. It took us some time, but we found our way.

Tell her to be sure to get his social security number. A judge will make him support his child, and he'll give her some money to help her, too. I know she's scared, but she can make it.

He wants to go back to his single life with freedom and no commitments? He should have thought about that before he asked her to marry him and before he made a baby. Now he wants to walk away because he wants to party and go with other girls

No. God ain't gon' bless him. You don't do that.

Hoodies

Notes on the Fourth Amendment

young fellas
create
cozy spaces
beneath
hoodies

just add music
via Bose beats,
and the warmth
creates
a mobile
man cave

some men
in their cars,
turn up tunes
and take off
on a road trip's
respite

some men
go for a run

with music streaming
through ear buds
soothing mind
body and soul

some men
take walks
in their portable refuges
hoodies up
out for strolls
to *de-stress*

yesterday
i learned about
the Fourth Amendment,
the right to privacy,
the right
to be left alone

supreme hearings,
supreme minds,
sharing scholarly
as well as personal
thoughts on the right
to be left alone

i'd honestly
never heard of
such a thing,
lovely,
really

treasuring my
me time
this new morning,
early spring,
tender
in its existence

in my
pink *hoodie*
I try,
as a writer,
to enter into
creative space

Sade streams in
through headphones
and inspires,
sunlight
through window panes
finds its way in

soothing mornings
monk-like
and
on a mission,
writing

entering into creative,
sacred space
in search of,

still,
the nonexistent,
perfect slant
of light

i think i can see why the brothers like their *hoodies*

it's warm
beneath hoods,
soothing,
heaven,
hidden

an escape . . .
flight from
microaggressions
and the stress
of male responsibilities
for a moment

the secret is out,
the brothers
know,
like none of us others
that . . .

it's cozy, warm, and comfy
beneath a *hoodie,*
a resting space
where one is soothed
and inspired,
a happy place

one young woman wrote:
"men should not wear
hoods,
should take them off
and be less
scary . . ."

cowl,
from the Latin,
means "hood," and
hooded cloaks
offer greater warmth
in monastic life

European Catholic and
Anglican monks are
snug in hooded habits
as long hours pass
in unheated
and drafty churches

the *hoodie,* too,
is the preferred
urban fashion
perfect for Chicago
and New York City
winters

it is cozy wear
that travels well

from the country
to the city
across the world
and to Miami

where Trayvon, in a *hoodie,*
and with a pack of Skittles,
lost
the right to privacy,
the right
to be left alone

they, too, sing, America

Go Lightly

1. I was around four. I don't know why, I just didn't want to go into his house. He touched little girls and gave them twenty-five cents for candy. I stood outside his door and waited for my friends to come out. I promised them I would wait for them.

2. Quite often I waited at the Junius Street elevated train station in Brooklyn for my aunt. She'd come home from the city and tell me all about her day at work. When I got old enough I would ride into the city on my own and wait for her after work. She'd take me shopping in Manhattan and to dinner afterward.

3. One time I listened and watched the grown-ups panic and try to help a man who had been shot. They screamed and wondered what was taking the ambulance so long to come. Someone said the ambulance doesn't come to neighborhoods like ours. The man who had been shot died there on the ground right in front of me.

4. Mr. Hayes' store was on the corner of our block. I loved going there on my own. I could go there and order my favorite toasted corn muffin with butter and jam with a glass of milk. I loved sitting there at the lunch counter. I took my sweet time eating and talking to Mr. Hayes while he washed dishes in the sink beneath the counter. My mom would pay the bill when she next came by.

5. At five the educators put me in first grade. They said I had already learned by watching Sesame Street what they were going to teach me. I always feel like I missed out on the naps by skipping kindergarten.

6. My mom and siblings were funny and smart and loved in our neighborhood, so nobody bothered me. When someone tried, I'd often hear, "That's Magic's sister. She's cool." And then the thug would move on. Magic was my brother's nick name because he wanted so much to play basketball like Magic Johnson from the Los Angeles Lakers.

7. Skipping kindergarten put me on a track for gifted students. I suppose they were young, those public school teachers in 1970s Brooklyn with their ideas of equality and belief in the powers of a good education. They came to work in our neighborhood and taught us our ABCs and 123s. In time, we graduated to Shakespeare and trigonometry. In high school on school trips, we visited the Metropolitan Museum of Art and the Hayden Planetarium and took long walks in Central Park, and they pointed to places on maps in geography class whispering of cultures and places far, far away giving us more room to dream.

8. I somehow found my way into a small private college away from home: Wagner. Most have never heard of it, but it was perfect. My world literally changed overnight. The opportunity to further my education created wonderful professional opportunities for me. Wagner College is also on a beautiful campus. It's serene and spacious there. My absolute favorite is the Burke Library. I would sit in the

library and gaze out of the floor-to-ceiling windows and dream sometimes when I was supposed to be studying. And sometimes I would sneak into the theater on campus and watch the theater students rehearse for an upcoming performance. It was magical being at Wagner. "We hope we've earned your friendship," is what was written in a letter signed by the president of the college that accompanied my undergraduate degree in economics.

9. Work in Corporate America followed allowing me to get a place in a nice neighborhood, so I didn't have to go back to the ghetto, after graduation. In the ghetto, the super markets were different. The fruits and veggies were lacking in abundance, and the ones that were there were not fresh. (How did they arrive not fresh?) The trash wasn't picked up regularly, and we had to strategically plan our outdoor activities in order to avoid shoot-outs. That was back in the day when one could know, more or less, when the shoot-outs would start. That was around sunset. I don't know what the strategy is now that the shoot-outs are more sporadic. Since I don't live there. Anymore I haven't got my ear to the ground to give me an advantage to strategize. But being aware of my surroundings and being careful in general still serves me well no matter where I go in the world.

10. In the communities I find myself in these days, the neighbors concern themselves with dog poop being scooped up, whether or not there is a good gym in their luxury apartment buildings, and if there is a doorman responsible enough to receive packages for goodies ordered online.

11. I quit my job in banking. Sometimes the environment felt more hostile than the shoot 'em up neighborhood

I grew up in. What most folks don't know is that the people who live in the ghetto are afraid of or are fed up with the thugs. So there is a community of people looking out for one another and a spirit of help. In the 'hood there is always the possibility of losing your life so one tends to be conscious and careful. In the corporate world one can lose one's heart and soul when not paying attention, so one has to be careful to take care. I quit that gig anyway. It was a drag.

12. It's taken some time to find my way. I stumbled into my first love. Turns out all those after school afternoons dreaming over teen magazines and getting lost in young adult novels signaled something I didn't even know existed. That is that one can grow up and be a writer. So I write now. Far less money. More freedom of movement and a lighter heart.

13. I skip town when I can: tapas in Madrid, cava in Barcelona, beer in Berlin, walks in forests in Finland, sitting beside lakes in Sweden . . .

14. Wherever you go, there you are. I had dreams of being a professional success: a career in business, a house, a car. I was looking forward to enjoying these perks of success. I believe the cracks in my dreams lets the light in and that peace and freedom are the ultimate perks. I once read something that said, "Go lightly dear you & don't try so hard."

What's in the Barn?

Andie awakes and sees that her husband isn't beside her. She gets out of bed and explores the farmhouse to see where he is. She finds no lights on and the children still sound asleep in their beds. Through the living room window, she sees a light shining out in the barn.

Walking outside in her nightgown across the field separating the house and the barn, she cautiously pulls open the barn door, peeks in, and sees her husband.

"What are you doing here?" she says.

"Did I wake you?" he asks with a concerned look on his face.

"No, no honey. I just woke up and reached for you and you weren't there. Your side of the bed was empty."

"You don't have any shoes on." Anthony, looking down at his wife's feet, could see from a distance. He takes the cashmere blanket draped over his shoulders, walks toward the barn door, and wraps her in it. Stepping out of his fleece slippers, he gestures for Andie to put them on.

Andie rubs her eyes as if she could remove her sleepiness from them with her touch and steps into the slippers.

"Are the children awake?" Anthony asks.

"No," she answers in a groggy, hushed tone.

Andie tiptoes a little further into the barn and tries to look over her husband's shoulder, mildly curious and slightly suspicious of what he is doing.

"I'm. . ." Anthony pauses and hangs his head, embarrassed.

Andie widens her eyes while looking up at her husband, as if her reaction would allow her to hear what he is reluctant to say.

"I'm...I'm trying to write a story," he finally gets it out.

"What?" Andie hears him, but she's not sure if she hears him properly.

He owns up to it again. "I'm trying to write."

"But you don't write," she responds, puzzled, in a way that's not quite clearly a statement or a question, her eyes searching his for clarification.

He hangs his head, and before he can get another word in, it comes to her in an instant.

Gingerly, cloaked in the soft wool blanket, Andie steps even further inside the barn and slowly walks toward the small card table Anthony has set up with his computer and a little lamp on top. She recognizes the lamp from their guest room.

She leans over in the predawn coolness of the morning and squints at the computer screen. Reading the first few paragraphs of his writing, she considers it for a moment, straightens up, and turns to face him. Anthony wants to disappear from embarrassment.

Standing in front of her husband, she looks him in the eye and lets him know her opinion. "It's good."

On her tippy toes, Andie kisses her husband full on the lips, walks back toward the barn door, and leaves.

Having wanted to die from embarrassment and deep insecurity about the desire to write stories, Anthony lets out a sigh and sits back down at the table in the chilly barn to begin to write again.

Some minutes later, he hears a sound of someone coming toward the barn entrance. His wife walks in again and carefully places a steaming cup of coffee on the table with just the right amount of cream and sugar the way he loves it. He sees she has brought the portable heater as well. She plugs it in and then leaves again.

The Hunted

Daniel lifted his head from Thieme's *Atlas of Anatomy* and slid his glasses off, turning his ear toward the door. Being inside warm and cozy during rain storms was one of his favorite things to do. He wondered, *Is that the doorbell? Who would be out in this rain?*

His grandmother constantly reminds him that he spends too much time inside. "Go out some time," she tells him. "You gotta work hard and play hard in this life," was one of her mantras.

But today would not be ideal. At the sound of the doorbell he wondered, *What fool would dare to wander out in rain like this?*

He walked over to the door and opened it, and there she was.

It was a shock really, a terrible shock to see her standing there in the rain with a gash on her head and blood streaming down her face. The first thing he thought was, *That's a nasty cut—it may need some stitches.*

She was thoroughly wet, her clothes all soaked through. It was as if she were dressed in a kind of cling wrap the way her clothes clung to every inch of her body, every curve and contour. Daniel thought, *She's exquisite.*

"You deaf?" Nana interrupted his thoughts. "Who is it?" His grandmother appeared at his side, ducked under his arm that was holding on to the frame of the door, and spotted the wet and bleeding stranger.

"Girl, you done lost your mind! Get in here!" Nana yelled while pulling the nearly naked young woman in from the freezing rain.

There weren't many things that made Nana nervous, not after all her years in nursing and all the living she'd done. She'd seen distraught young women quietly trying to hold back their sobbing. She'd tended to women in torn clothes and even some who have been soaked to the bone in rain water. But this stranger who showed up on her doorstep in tears and ripped clothing and with bare feet cut up and bleeding in the rain storm shook her.

"Daniel, call 911, baby!"

Daniel knew his grandmother all too well. He could hear the fear in her voice despite her tough talk as he got through to the emergency operator.

Nana lead the girl to the sofa, reached for a cashmere throw, and wrapped her in it. "Daniel!" she shouted. "What's wrong with you? Get me some towels! You the medicine man. Why I got to tell you everything?" *Medicine Man* is Nana's nick name for him, which masked her pride of her grandson who recently began medical school.

"Girl, what has happened?" Nana spoke to the wet creature softly all along looking into her eyes.

The young lady began to speak but was interrupted when Daniel returned with the towels. Nana realized that she had better get the girl into some warm, dry clothes. "I'm gonna get you outta these wet things. That alright with you?"

The young lady, between shivers and chattering teeth, nodded yes.

"What's your name?" Nana wanted to know.

She managed to chatter out, "Jeannie."

"Well come on, Jeannie, let's get you out of these soaking wet clothes. What kind of crazy you mixed up in? You done something wrong? Let me know now! The ambulance is on its way, but I'll call the cops on you too!" Nana searched her eyes for some signal as to how to proceed.

The young lady made a movement of her head and parted her lips as if to respond, but nothing came out.

"I don't know what that means," Nana let her know.

Daniel stood out of the way by the bedroom door while Nana sat the girl down. Nana could be rough, but he knew this girl was in good hands. The best actually.

Pondering this strange, wet, bruised creature that had shown up on their doorstep, he found himself mesmerized. Normally there was a calmness about him. Not much fazed him. It worked both ways: he was not unsettled easily or easily moved.

He mused to himself, *There's nothing in the medical books that addresses the shock that comes over first-year medical students when a gorgeous, bruised woman shows up at one's door.*

Nana closed the door with him on the other side of it, interrupting his thoughts. She opened it quickly again as he was stepping away and whispered, "Keep an eye out for the EMTs."

Standing over Jeannie who was sitting on the bed, Nana lifted Jeannie's arms up in the air and pulled her wet silk T-shirt up and off. While Jeannie stood up she wrapped her arms around Nana's shoulders and stepped out of her pajama-like silk bottoms and then put on the cotton night shirt that Nana had given to her to cover up.

Jeannie was beginning to gain her composure a bit and said through her diminishing tears, "First, I was silly enough to lock myself out of my house. And . . . then when I tried to climb through the window I slipped and gashed my head. I cut my feet as well. How awful is it?"

"You can speak," Nana teased her as she sat next to her on the bed. She gently wiped Jeannie's face with a soft towel to dry her tears.

"You'll need to calm down now or your face is bound to swell up even more from so much crying. Maybe this here cream with aloe vera will keep the swelling down." Nana, keeping with the quiet that had taken over the room, spoke in a whisper as she gently rubbed the cream on Jeannie's face.

Daniel showed the paramedics the way to the bedroom when they arrived. He watched as the girl and Nana talked with them. One of the paramedics reached for the telephone and made a call while the other skillfully cleaned Jeannie's wounds even more thoroughly. Before packing up to leave, he placed a bandage over the cut on her head, which turned out to be bloodier than deep.

He certainly keeps his distance, Jeannie thought to herself as she looked up and saw Daniel standing in the corner. Her heart pounded incredibly quickly inside her chest. Seeing him this close up took her breath away.

"So she'll be alright?" Nana asked the paramedics.

"Yes, ma'am, she'll be fine. Just bruised and terribly sore I imagine. We've asked her to come in first thing in the morning just to run a few tests for precautionary measures, but she'll be alright." The paramedics confided in Nana on their way out.

"Daniel, can you walk Jeannie home? The paramedics called her house and spoke with her brother. He's at home now waiting for her. They moved into the Johanson's old house just down the street."

With great care, Daniel took Jeannie's hand and gently placed his arms around her waist. She even smells good, he thought.

He was grateful that the rain had stopped making it easier for her to walk outdoors with his help.

"Just a few doors down?" he confirmed with Jeannie in regards to her home.

"Yes," she whimpered in response.

"Oh you are our new neighbors?"

Before Jeannie could respond Daniel asked, "Is that him? Is that your brother at the door of your house?"

Jeannie nodded her head as she walked with her head on Daniel's shoulder as he supported her.

Standing in front of their house holding the door open, Jeannie's brother couldn't believe what he was seeing.

Gingerly, Daniel handed Jeannie over to her brother keeping an eye on her as she struggled to stand on her own. He asked her, "Is it alright if I come by tomorrow to see how you are or if I can help in any way?"

Jeannie nodded signaling a pitiful yes and then disappeared into her house with her brother closing the door behind them.

Overwhelmed with a mix of emotions, Daniel took his time getting back home. Shaken, he allowed himself to rest in knowing she'd be alright, and that he could see her tomorrow.

Inside Jeannie's house, her brother was furious with her. "Well, I hope you got what you wanted." He spits out.

"It worked didn't it? He's coming over tomorrow."

One Who Waits

A Meditation

What summons us to a place, and how shall we live? Often we have little idea how best to answer these questions, as if a conspiring universe is calling us out and asking the questions. Life is brief and the future is uncertain and full of mystery.

Poetic encouragements tell us to leave the familiar for a while and change rooms in our minds. By doing so, sometimes we can stumble toward messy answers to the questions—toward an understanding or knowing of some kind. In the meantime, before we can get to the answers, we need to live the questions . . .

This can be scary. Our bodies carry memories of being small, vulnerable creatures surrounded by the unknown. When confronted with the unknown, we may choose to withdraw to a more sheltered place. But when we strip away familiar comforts, we may find ourselves more exposed and open to and accepting of change.

I find myself in Finland for a season, in the midst of alternating land and water, lakes and rivers. There is space. And, too, there are forests in abundance.

With a backdrop of cool grays and light hues, the sensible, subtle gentleness of the mornings gives way to enigmatic, dark afternoons, which creep in after only a few hours of daylight. Signaled by colorful sunsets, which offer the most color of the day, I soon find myself again wandering along moonlit forest trails or up steep stairs into an evening's candlelit rooms, enchanted. In the darkness, my imagination comes alive.

All is warm and toasty indoors in Finland. Earnest, thoughtful preparation for long, cold winters is historic here, and this fosters ethereal and comfortable evenings that are perfect for dreaming, allowing creativity and fantasy to bloom.

These evenings are ideal for penning stories, meditations, or poems:

ONE WHO WAITS

it's never too long
to wait
for something
good

for relief, like a sigh,
from a misty darkness
when snow is missing,
I wait

midnight whispers offer
morning surprises
of silent snow

slipping in on silken slippers
orchestrating ice crystal
moments

sweet, small miracles,
like diamond dust,
are sprinkled on branches
and floating
in air

cooling droplets,
like champagne bubbles,
lift my spirits,
summoning in
anticipated change

it's never too long
to wait
for something
good

Dream a New Dream

Sophia shuffled her feet, pushed her sunglasses closer to her eyes, and fussed with her powder-blue silk shorts, before she took a deep breath, lowered her head, and rang the doorbell.

When PJ opened the door, Sophia said in her soft voice, "You have a porch."

"I know!" PJ squealed. "Isn't it cool?"

"It's supercool.

PJ stepped out the door of her home and joined Sophia on the porch. "I come out here when it's raining and just plop down and watch the rain."

"Exactly. I would do the same thing. It's like you can get a little closer to nature. We should have lunch out here next time it rains."

"Fantastic idea! Come on in." PJ jumped up and held the door open for Sophia.

They found PJ's mom, Fanny, in the kitchen. "Mom, this is Sophia, my friend I told you about, from school."

"Hi, Sophia. Do you like strawberry daiquiris? We're having them with brunch."

Sophia shuttered at the thought of brunch, of gathering at the table and everything. They had no idea how much she really couldn't do that. Even the thought of it was painful to her. She tried to think of an excuse so she could be gone by then.

"Mom, you remember . . ." PJ leaned in, widening her eyes at her mother. "You said we could eat in my room."

"I remember, sweetie. Just remember to bring down the plates. The last thing I want is to find them up there two weeks from now."

Sophia shuffled and said, "That would be pretty awful."

Fanny smiled in Sophia's direction, taking in that she barely spoke above a whisper. "Sophia, PJ tells me you have the prettiest eyes."

Sophia looked over at PJ, who realized she was getting used to Sophia looking at her through her sunglasses.

"Mom!" PJ couldn't believe her mom had repeated this. She'd mentioned the sunglasses just as a kind of heads-up.

Sophia's heart began to beat a little faster and she nervously lowered her head. Fanny gently lifted Sophia's face, as if she were touching feathers. She glided her hands across Sophia's cheeks. Sophia was beginning to shiver like she did when she got supernervous.

Fanny reached for Sophia's sunglasses and gently slid them off.

Sophia's eyes glistened with pools of tears.

Fanny saw the tears and quietly wondered, what has this dear child been through?

She folded the sunglasses and placed them in Sophia's hands. "You do have the prettiest eyes," she said. "Stunning really." A moment later, she added, to PJ's astonishment, "You are safe here." Then, without skipping a beat, she asked, "What are you girls drinking?"

PJ had to push past her amazement. Her own nervousness dissipated in love at her mother's words. "Frozen daiquiris! Oh, Mom, please!" And turning to Sophia, she said, "My mom makes these mean strawberry daiquiris!"

"Virgin, of course," Fanny added. "Sophia, would you like to try one? Do. I think you'll absolutely love it!"

Sophia smiled a wide, shy yes, and the tears that glittered in her eyes spilled out and streamed into her smile. She gasped.

PJ took Sophia by the hand, and just before the girls began to run up to her room, Sophia pulled back on PJ's hand to slow her a bit. "I get them from my mother," she said, looking back at Fanny. "My mom had the same eyes."

Fanny let the strawberries slip through her fingers and fall back into the bowl of water. She turned toward Sophia. "Where is your mom now? At home?"

Sophia looked down, shuffled her feet, and twisted her lips, fighting back more tears. "She died a few months ago."

"I'm sorry to hear that. Who do you live with, your father?"

"No."

The room was heavy with silence. It stayed that way for what seemed like forever to Sophia. Tears now ran from her eyes. She broke the silence, "How about one of those strawberry daiquiris?"

"Double dose of virgin strawberry daiquiris coming right up!"

Sophia's nervousness and anxiety, and her low sense of self, always lessened as soon as she walked through the door of her home. Her sadness wasn't as big. It would begin to dissipate. When she got in from school, she would switch on a floor lamp with a muted and cozy glow, which she might enhance by lighting some candles. She'd then sit down on the parquet floor and exhale deeply in an effort to relax. Luckily, today the after-school sun streamed in through the windows, lifting her spirits.

A few record albums were strewn around the room. This allowed her to easily choose a tune from among her favorites. A Joni Mitchell song frequently did nicely.

Their plan had been simple: make it through high school and get into a good college. She had to keep her grades up. A full academic scholarship was the goal. What they had talked about. She'd done that. She'd already been accepted by her dream college. She could check that one off the list.

High school was all but finished, so next she just had to get through university. Her mind didn't wander to afterward. One step at a time. Besides, that was as far as their talks had gotten. The rest she would have to figure out on her own.

Her aloneness filled the room as it had for the past few months. She was on her own, and that was all there was to it. "*Count your blessings.*" She could hear the sound of her mother's voice in her mind. She was lucky not to have to go into foster care or an orphanage. That was a blessing. One easy to count.

She'd had her eighteenth birthday in December, so they let her live on her own—and would pay for it until she finished high school. Food and shelter, safe from the outside world. Another blessing to count.

She'd picked out most of the furniture herself. She had particular taste, knowing something about vintage furniture from all the hours she'd spent cruising flea markets with her mother.

Sophia felt lucky, as if her mother were still looking out for her. And if her memory of her mother ever began to fade, she'd just have to pick up one of her diaries. All the details of their days together were there: the films they watched, the music they listened to, their taste in fashion, where they bought a few things or saved a little money, their bank accounts, recipes for their favorite dishes. All of it was written there, in her mom's diaries. Sophia had read them incessantly since her passing, in the desire to keep fresh in her mind the stories, hopes, and dreams that they created together. It was all there.

There was even more evidence of a guardian angel. Sophia inherited a trunk that her mom had in storage. It contained things Sophia now felt she simply couldn't live without: more of her mom's diaries, a stack of albums, a record player, DVDs, and clothes from when her mom was just a little older than she was now.

A social worker paid for the things Sophia wanted, or needed, from the allowance she received from the city. She went to Goodwill to find some of her furnishings, pretty sure that other stores wouldn't have what she was looking for. She found a rose-colored velvet sofa and a bone-white distressed wooden dresser with glass cabinet doors. She thought she could put her mom's dresses, skirts, blouses, and trousers in it. Her mom's silk lingerie would fit nicely in the first two little drawers.

Her mom's albums—the ones not scattered on the floor—were placed with her diaries on the middle shelf, at eye level so she could reach them easily.

Loneliness and depression presented themselves fully and often, but fulfilling the responsibilities of her studies helped to keep them smaller than they might otherwise be. She especially liked, and excelled in, her French class.

Sophia wrote all the time, on anything she could get her hands on: notebooks, napkins, the backs of documents. Blog posts written under her nom de plume, Coo Coo, helped to alleviate her loneliness too.

Coo Coo was what her mom had called her affectionately, and since the kids at school thought she was nuts, she thought it was a perfect pen name. She was fascinated with all things French and titled her blog *The Paris Degenerates*. It focused on poets, writers, and artists who had gone to live in Paris. That was her ultimate dream, to live and work in Paris—or, rather, the dream she'd shared with her mother. They were planning for it together. Now it was up to her to keep the dream alive, or somehow figure out how to dream a new dream. . . .

About the Author

Tinka Harvard is a writer and theologian. She is a graduate of Wagner College and has a master's in divinity from Union Theological Seminary at Columbia University in New York City. She offers her intellectual talents in preaching, inspirational speaking, workshops, and retreats.

Her writing has appeared most recently in publications including *StepAway Magazine, Adelaide Literary Magazine, Adelaide Voices Anthology 2018,* and *Polychrome Ink.*

To learn more, please visit www.tinkaharvard.com.

Made in the USA
Middletown, DE
18 August 2018